FIRST EDITION

Bioethics in Physical Therapy

A Reader

EDITED BY

Katherine K. Johnson

Bellarmine University

SAN DIEGO

Bassim Hamadeh, CEO and Publisher
Jennifer Codner, Senior Field Acquisitions Editor
Anne Jones, Project Editor
Casey Hands, Production Editor
Emely Villavicencio, Senior Graphic Designer
Alexa Lucido, Licensing Manager
Natalie Piccotti, Director of Marketing
Kassie Graves, Vice President of Editorial
Jamie Giganti, Director of Academic Publishing

Cover image: Copyright © 2021 iStockphoto LP/shulz.

Printed in the United States of America.

3970 Sorrento Valley Blvd., Ste. 500, San Diego, CA 92121

To Mom and Dad, with gratitude

CONTENTS

ACKNOWLEDGMENTS

I want to thank Cognella Academic Publishing for the opportunity to fulfill my goal of publishing a text about bioethics. I was fortunate to work with Anne Jones. Her constant support and practical guidance helped me set realistic and achievable goals.

Thanks to my colleagues, students, and anonymous reviewers for reading drafts of the book. I am especially grateful to Joseph "Tony" Brosky, Beth Ennis, Elizabeth Ulanowski, Beth Quinn, Laura Lee "Dolly" Swisher, and Nancy Kirsch for talking to me about the practical difficulties of the healthcare world from the perspective of a physical therapist. I am fortunate to be able to include original pieces by Nancy Kirsch and Matthew Pianalto, whose perspectives have enriched the book.

I owe a special debt of gratitude to Steven Millar, who read, edited, and commented on everything I wrote in this book. Finally, I thank my husband, my son, and my family for their love and support. I am, indeed, fortunate to have such a wonderful family.

INTRODUCTION

Understanding the basics of ethics is essential for a physical therapist. Diagnostic skills, technical expertise, and knowledge of the body are not enough; being a good clinician requires a moral education as well. Ethics is the study of right action. Ethics provides the tools to pursue a larger goal of living a good life. An ethics education helps you develop a deeper understanding of moral principles and their theoretical basis. When you understand why some behaviors are right and others are wrong, you will be better prepared to decide hard cases, neutralize moral confusion, and interpret new conflicts. Cultivating a moral imagination will enable you to recognize the moral dimensions of everyday situations. This disposition will aid in maneuvering through complexities and help prevent bad actions, harm to others, and troublesome habits.

The goal of this reader is twofold: to stimulate your moral imagination and to help you be ethically prepared to respond to a conflict. As a healthcare worker, learning to exercise your moral imagination will improve your ability to navigate complex and challenging ethical situations in practice. Learning skills such as moral reflection, awareness, and sensitivity will enhance your ability to perceive the ethical contours of practice. This book does not teach you what to think about specific situations, and its goal is not to tell you what to choose. Rather, the objective is to help you decipher the meaning of moral principles, activate your moral imagination, and rediscover your moral conscience. Achieving these goals will reorient and embolden you to effectively respond to moral conflicts and crises.

Moral principles are guides to action. They provide direction and shed light on the moral dimensions of conduct. For example, the biomedical principle of autonomy tells us to respect the self-governing nature of competent persons. Such moral principles help us to evaluate choices and actions. They even help us to choose how to respect the autonomy of an incompetent patient.

You likely possess your own personal morality, a set of informal rules that guide your actions. However, as part of the healthcare profession, you are also subject to other, even higher, moral standards. You must follow the ethical standards and values of the physical therapy profession. These values include accountability, altruism, collaboration, compassion/caring, duty, excellence, integrity, and social responsibility.[1]

The moral imagination is a faculty, a mental capability, that facilitates moral decisions. It extends beyond simply following rules and principles, even those dictated by your profession. The moral imagination motivates ethical insight. It is the capacity that enables us to make sense of our experiences and to imagine new ways to maximize our moral values and fulfill our ethical commitments.[2] The moral imagination enriches our moral vision, and it does not allow for the kinds of self-deceptive thinking that leads to ethical compromise. Just as we would exercise a muscle, so we must develop our moral imagination in order to make it strong and useful.

A good clinician must cultivate the moral imagination. To be ethical, one must know the good, choose the good, and do the good. Most people have a conscience, but not all of us follow its advice and warnings. A well-developed moral imagination enables healthcare workers to cultivate ethical sensitivity, to develop ethical awareness, and to identify different perspectives. As a creative capacity, the moral imagination empowers us to be adaptive, to look beyond the clinical features of a situation, and to acknowledge the relevant values and ethical principles at stake.

The moral imagination is proactive, inventive, and reflective. It helps us to see possibility and opportunity. As an insightful faculty, the moral imagination can help us to meet the moral commitments of the profession and to recognize when professional rules fail to provide enough guidance in a context-specific situation. Effective decision-making is not merely a formulaic process; failure to properly assess concrete situations and contextualize moral principles impedes responsible moral action. The moral imagination facilitates a creative yet critical perspective to help us perceive opportunity despite structural barriers. Developing your moral imagination will help you to recognize your limits, observe opportunity, and discern the moral point of view.

References

American Physical Therapy Association. *Code of Ethics for the Physical Therapist*. Updated August 12, 2021. https://www.apta.org/siteassets/pdfs/policies/codeofethicshods06-20-28-25.pdf

Johnson, Mark. *Moral Imagination: Implications of Cognitive Science for Ethics*. University of Chicago Press, 1993.

Werhane, Patricia H. *Moral Imagination and Management Decision-Making*. Oxford University Press, 1999.

---

[1] American Physical Therapy Association, *Code of Ethics for the Physical Therapist*, updated August 12, 2020. https://www.apta.org/siteassets/pdfs/policies/codeofethicshods06-20-28-25.pdf

[2] Mark Johnson, *Moral Imagination: Implications of Cognitive Science for Ethics* (Chicago: University of Chicago Press, 1993); Patricia H. Werhane, *Moral Imagination and Management Decision-Making* (New York: Oxford University Press, 1999).

UNIT 1

A Crash Course in Ethics

Ada's Story

Ada is a pediatric physical therapist specializing in the care of children with disabilities. She works at a private care facility that participates in an annual weekend community clinic providing free care to kids. At the clinic, Ada evaluates Michael, an 18-month-old boy with Down syndrome. Michael exhibits physical developmental delays common with his genetic condition: he has underdeveloped motor skills, awkward movement, and poor coordination. Despite the complications, Michael's prognosis is positive. Ada believes that if Michael receives immediate and regular therapy, his physical delays will dramatically improve. His independence will increase, and chances of future injury will decrease. Ada learns that Michael and his family entered the United States illegally a few months ago, and his parents do not have the money to pay for his medical needs. Ada's clinic manager informs her that the clinic is struggling financially and cannot accept any more pro bono cases. In order to continue to serve patients and protect employees, the clinic must focus its resources on those who can pay.

Schema Activation/Response Question

What does Ada's role as a healthcare provider require of her?

Cultivating Professional Values

The APTA core values aim to promote good reasoning. The key values at stake in Ada's story include:

- **Accountability:** taking responsibility for one's actions and choices
- **Altruism:** sacrificing for others and putting others' needs before your own
- **Collaboration:** working together in pursuit of a shared goal
- **Compassion/Caring:** having kindness and finding importance in the suffering of others
- **Duty:** fulfilling one's commitment to the profession and meeting the public's trust
- **Excellence:** possessing knowledge and skill and acquiring habits of lifelong learning

- **Integrity:** acting in accord with one's personal and professional moral identity
- **Social Responsibility:** doing good for others and helping the larger community

Introduction to the Topic

Moral philosophy seeks to answer questions about how we ought to live. What makes an act right? What makes a person good? What is valuable? What does morality require of us? Ethics provides the tools that healthcare providers need to answer these questions. Studying ethics helps clinicians cultivate practices and mindsets that render good judgments, decisions that align with their moral values and professional obligations. While the study of ethics can be very helpful, answering ethical questions can be a challenge.

The first step toward ethical behavior requires an understanding of the moral tools available to us. This unit introduces students to four moral theories and the principles of biomedical ethics. By learning these various theories, clinicians can extrapolate effectively. The principles facilitate meaningful decision-making strategies for exercising good judgement. Without an understanding of ethics, our ability to make good decisions is restricted, and we are unable to act according to our values.

Introduction to the Readings

Utilitarianism, Deontology, and Virtue Ethics

I wrote the first reading, *"Three Classical Moral Theories: Critical Frameworks for Deliberation,"* to introduce readers to three prominent ethical theories that have developed in the Western world: Utilitarianism, Deontology, and Virtue Ethics. I examine the views of three paradigmatic philosophers who represent each theory. My goal is to describe their theoretical frameworks, to sketch the nature of our moral commitments, and to "provide a foundation for critical analysis of complex real-world issues."

The first theory I discuss is Utilitarianism, a consequentialist moral theory that claims the rightness and wrongness of an act is based on outcomes. British philosopher John Stuart Mill (1806–1873) was one of the greatest defenders of Utilitarianism. According to Mill, the sole command of morality is the Principle of Utility. This principle-based theory instructs us to maximize the greatest amount of happiness for the greatest number of beings. Mill recognizes that morality is a social endeavor. Our actions affect others, and we ought to evaluate behaviors by calculating their positive and negative outcomes not simply for ourselves but also for the community.

Deontology is another principle-based theory that provides a duty-based account of morality. German philosopher Immanuel Kant (1724–1804) developed one of the earliest formulations of this theory. In contrast to Utilitarianism, deontologists claim that one's motives for acting, rather than substantive outcomes, determine the moral worth of an act. Only duty, and not self-interest or personal gain, should fuel and provoke action. Kant claims that morally good conduct must be directed by the dictates of reason. The Categorical Imperative, Kant's supreme principle of morality, codifies various formulas for morality that commands universality, consistency, rationality, and respect.

Virtue Ethics originates in ancient Greece, particularly in the works of Aristotle (384–322 BCE), one of the most celebrated figures in the history of philosophy. Unlike Utilitarianism and Deontology that endorse universal and uniform principles of action, Aristotle proposes a character-based approach to morality. He redirects how we think about right and wrong and highlights the connection between action, character, and emotion. Aristotle describes how a good person is a virtuous person. The virtues, he explains, are desirable character traits that help us to flourish and to achieve happiness. Morality, thus, involves the cultivation of virtuous dispositions, namely excellences of character, that enable us to live well.

Noddings's Ethics of Care

The second reading, selections from "Why Care About Caring," by contemporary feminist philosopher Nel Noddings (1929–) draws from her book *Caring: A Relational Approach to Ethics and Moral Education*. Noddings presents an ethics of care, a moral theory centered around interdependency and modelled on the mother–child relationship. She defends the significance of a care-based approach to morality because, she claims, we are inescapably intertwined in the lives of others. For Noddings, morality must acknowledge relationships as a permanent fixture of life. An ethics of care recognizes the values that are at stake in community with others.

Noddings's approach to morality is motivated by the work of Carol Gilligan, a psychologist specializing in the study of moral development.[1] Gilligan objected to previous views about moral development that had been proposed by Lawrence Kohlberg. He claimed that moral development coincided with cognitive development.[2] Moral understanding, he said, progresses through a series of three stages. In the first stage, the preconventional level, a child sees morality in connection to consequences and punishment. In the second stage, the conventional level, a child sees morality as acceptance of social rules. In the third stage, the postconventional level, a child understands the nature of universal moral principles and can think through ethics on their own. Kohlberg claimed that most people do not achieve the third level; rather, most people adopt moral conventions from those around them.

Gilligan disputed Kohlberg's findings, arguing that he failed to take into account the female perspective. Gilligan noticed that while the male and female subjects in her study often came to the

---

[1] Carol Gilligan, *In a Different Voice: Psychological Theory and Women's Development* (Cambridge, MA: Harvard University Press, 1982).

[2] Lawrence Kohlberg, *Essays on Moral Development* (New York: Harper & Row, 1981).

same conclusions, they typically had different reasons for their choices. Gilligan noted a distinction between an impersonal, principle-based moral reasoning typical of the male subjects and a personal, relationship-based moral thinking typical of the female subjects. Noddings draws her insights about ethics from Gilligan's findings. While rational principles can be useful guides to conduct, nontangible and less abstract motivators, like empathy and sensitivity to others' needs, are also valuable structures for moral thinking and judgment.

Noddings stresses that an ethics of care diverges from traditional, principle-based models of ethics like Mill's and Kant's. Principle-based moral theories are individualistic, duty-oriented, impartial, and traditionally masculine. Noddings argues that these theories are "mathematical" and "fail to share with each other the feelings, the conflicts, the hopes and ideas that influence our eventual choices." In contrast, an ethics of care is community-based, relationship-oriented, partial, and distinctively feminine. Noddings's alternative approach to moral thinking emphasizes values that encompass our connections with others, notably values such as compassion, cooperation, integrity, solidarity, and conscientiousness. These feminine values contrast with the traditionally male ethical perspective that privileges values such as justice, rights, impartiality, and autonomy. Noddings explains that a care-based perspective is built upon the essential features and the "ethical reality" involved in relationships, specifically "in the relation between the one-caring and the cared-for."

Principles of Biomedical Ethics

I wrote the last reading, "*The Moral Pillars of Biomedical Ethics*," to present an overview of the four principles of biomedical ethics. These ethical standards guide healthcare workers as they navigate complex ethical problems and provide an ethical framework for clinicians to evaluate moral conflicts. The principles articulate ideals geared toward the protection of patient well-being. Beneficence, the first principle of biomedical ethics, articulates the value of human welfare, and requires providers to actively promote patient interests. Nonmaleficence, the second principle, codifies the 'do no harm' standard, and imposes a negative obligation that limits conduct. Respect for autonomy, the third ethical principle, honors the dignity of all people, and requires that providers treat people as self-governing and independent individuals. Finally, justice, the fourth principle, concerns the fair distribution of goods and the equitable treatment of patients. Justice involves a procedural approach for maximizing healthcare's limited resources.

The principles of biomedical ethics are not based on a particular moral tradition, such as the theories of Mill, Kant, Aristotle, and Noddings. However, these standards build upon and incorporate the ideals expressed by these philosophers. They describe and codify the norms of conduct and the moral expectations and obligations of the healthcare profession.

References

Gilligan, Carol. *In a Different Voice: Psychological Theory and Women's Development.* Harvard University Press, 1982.

Kohlberg, Lawrence. *Essays on Moral Development.* Harper & Row, 1981.

Three Classical Moral Theories

Critical Frameworks for Deliberation

By Katherine K. Johnson

Introduction

Ethics is a branch of philosophy that seeks answers to questions, such as: What is a good life? What are our moral duties? What is a right act? Ethics is concerned with how we ought to live.

The field of ethics has its skeptics. Because we often disagree about the right course of action, because we struggle to find common ground, and because we cannot always solve moral disputes, universal moral truths can seem dubious and unreliable. Many philosophers, however, have developed theories to defend the truths of moral philosophy. Ethics can provide answers. Ethics is complex, but it gives us useful tools for deliberating.

In this [reading], I explore three classical moral theories that attempt to explain our moral obligations and commitments. I follow three paradigmatic philosophers to draw out some of the unique and foundational features that distinguish each theory. My goal is to emphasize the valuable thinking strategies and the modes of ethical deliberation that each theory provides. These three theories give us constructive tools for ethical reasoning; they provide a foundation for the critical analysis of complex, real-world issues.

Utilitarianism

Utilitarianism is a consequentialist moral theory; it claims that the rightness and wrongness of actions are determined by their consequences. British philosopher John Stuart Mill (1806–1873) was one of history's greatest utilitarian thinkers. He proposed that the sole command of morality is found in one simple tenet, the principle of utility.

> The creed which accepts as the foundations of morals "utility" or the "greatest happiness principle" holds that actions are right in proportion as they tend to

promote happiness, wrong as they tend to produce the reverse of happiness. By happiness is intended pleasure and the absence of pain; by unhappiness, pain and the privation of pleasure.[1]

Mill resolves moral conflicts by using a principle-driven strategy to assess the rightness and wrongness of actions. He proposes that a person, by following the dictates of utility, can determine which course of action will benefit the greatest number of people. The act must produce a better balance of utility over harm for those affected. Mill stresses the importance of protecting the interests of all and not simply our own. Every person's welfare counts equally when weighing the consequences of an act.

As between his own happiness and that of others, utilitarianism requires him to be as strictly impartial as a disinterested and benevolent spectator. In the golden rule of Jesus of Nazareth, we read the complete spirit of the ethics of utility. "To do as you would be done by," and "to love your neighbor as yourself," constitute the ideal perfection of utilitarian morality. As the means of making the nearest approach to this ideal, utility would enjoin, first, that laws and social arrangements should place the happiness or (as, speaking practically, it may be called) the interest of every individual as nearly as possible in harmony with the interest of the whole; and, secondly, that education and opinion, which have so vast a power over human character, should so use that power as to establish in the mind of every individual an indissoluble association between his own happiness and the good of the whole […][2]

As a progressive social reformer, Mill believes that morality must be understood as a social enterprise. His Greatest Happiness Principle encourages the cultivation of other-regarding behaviors that promote both the good of society and the good of the individual. Mill argues that utility benefits the general welfare of society and maximizes the overall well-being of humanity. He is adamant that his moral theory is not egoistic; rather, it stresses equality and impartiality for everyone both directly and indirectly involved. Mill appeals to our desire for happiness and inspires individuals to cultivate tendencies that promote the good of their community.

Mill considers not only the stakeholders but also the nature of the goods—or pleasures—that result from an act. Mill does not merely weigh the quantity of goods produced; instead, he argues that a morally good act produces greater *quality* goods. Mill's theory is hedonistic; it endorses the view that pleasures are intrinsically valuable. However, he offers a qualitative account of pleasure to

---

[1] John Stuart Mill, *Utilitarianism*, 2nd ed. Edited by George Sher, (Indianapolis: Hackett Publishing Company, Inc., 2001), 7.
[2] Mill, *Utilitarianism*, 17.

include goods that *truly* benefit individuals. In the following passage, Mill presents the contented pig objection to illustrate qualitative hedonism.

> [F]or if the source of pleasure were precisely the same to human beings and to swine, the rule of life which is good enough for the one would be good enough for the other. The comparison of the Epicurean life to that of beasts is felt as degrading, precisely because a beast's pleasures do not satisfy a human being's conception of happiness. Human beings have faculties more elevated than the animal appetites and, when once made conscious of them, do not regard anything as happiness which does not include their gratification. [...] It is better to be a human being dissatisfied than a pig satisfied; better to be Socrates dissatisfied than a fool satisfied. And if the fool, or the pig, are of a different opinion, it is because they only know their own side of the question. The other party to the comparison knows both sides.[3]

Mill argues that to understand the moral force of utility requires the recognition of the quality of pleasures. For example, if we follow Utilitarianism, we will value social policies with lasting and sustained benefits over those with short-term gains. Enabling homeless individuals to find permanent homes and leave the cycle of homelessness will, for Mill, be more ethical than placing people in temporary overnight housing. To calculate utility simply on the quantity of goods is insufficient and incomplete. Rather, we must calculate the quality of the goods that can be produced and ask what act or policy will bring about the best overall and enduring state of affairs and happiness.

Utilitarianism offers insights about how utility can both guide social practices and help individuals cultivate empathetic and other-regarding habits that benefit one other. As we make ethical decisions, we can incorporate a utility-driven thinking strategy that calculates both benefits and risks and integrates the interests of everyone involved.

Deontology

A deontological moral framework uses a principle-driven strategy and stresses the ethical significance of duty and obligation. German philosopher Immanuel Kant (1724–1804) formulated the first Western account of deontological ethics. He argued that moral principles must codify absolute standards that allow no exceptions and are always binding on all people. He states: "Everyone must grant that a law, if it is to hold morally, that is, as a ground of obligation, must carry with it absolute necessity."[4]

---

[3] Mill, *Utilitarianism*, 8–10.

[4] Immanuel Kant, *The Cambridge Edition of the Works of Immanuel Kant: Practical Philosophy*. Translated and edited by Mary J. Gregor (New York: Cambridge University Press, 1996), 44 [4:389].

In contrast to Utilitarianism, Deontology is an approach to ethics that rejects the role of consequences in determining the morality of an act. Instead, Kant claims that duty is the proper motivation for moral conduct.

> An action from duty has its moral worth *not in the purpose* to be attained by it but in the maxim in accordance with which it is decided upon, and therefore does not depend upon the realization of the object of the action but merely upon the *principle of volition* in accordance with which the action is done without regard for any object of the faculty of desire.[5]

Kant describes how duty is not based on the mere appearance of an act but rather on what motivates the agent to act. Kant defends the view that we ought to do the right thing because it is our duty. Duty, and not unknown effects, is what ought to propel morally good conduct. When motivated by personal gain and not duty, we fail to do the right thing.

Kant asserts a principle of morality called the Categorical Imperative, which has numerous formulations. Its first formulation is "Act only in accordance with that maxim though which you can at the same time will that it become a universal law."[6] Kant says that we must only act on a maxim, a reason for action, if our reason can become a universal rule for everyone to consistently follow. A morally good act, he claims, must be universalizable, meaning that it must be an act that everyone is able to do. For example, we must never make false promises because when we do, we make an exception of ourselves.

The second formulation of the Categorical Imperative is: "So act that you use humanity, whether in our own person or in the person of any other, always at the same time as an end, never merely as a means."[7] This moral command requires that people respect one another. We must never use others for our own personal gain or to maximize our own self-interests.

> [Persons], therefore, are not merely subjective ends, the existence of which as an effect of our action has worth *for us*, but rather *objective ends*, that is, beings the existence of which is in itself an end, and indeed one such that no other end, to which they would serve *merely* as means, can be put in its place, since without it nothing of absolute worth would be found anywhere; [...] This principle of humanity, [...] is the supreme limiting condition of the freedom of action of every human being. [...][8]

---

[5] Kant, *The Cambridge Edition of the Works of Immanuel Kant: Practical Philosophy,* 55 [4:399–400].

[6] Kant, *The Cambridge Edition of the Works of Immanuel Kant: Practical Philosophy,* 73 [4:4:402; 4:421].

[7] Kant, *The Cambridge Edition of the Works of Immanuel Kant: Practical Philosophy,* 80 [4:429].

[8] Kant, *The Cambridge Edition of the Works of Immanuel Kant: Practical Philosophy,* 79 [4:428], 81 [4:431].

People possess intrinsic duty and worth. We can never take advantage of others merely to get what we want. Kant's point is that people, as rational beings and as ends in themselves, have a special dignity that must be honored. People are not mere instruments. For example, slavery is an oppressive practice that uses individuals for the sake of someone else's own interests. Slavery treats people as a means to the slaveholder's goals and, in so doing, violates the freedoms that we naturally possess as human beings. Acts that intentionally obstruct a person's independence are morally wrong and degrade the sanctity of rational beings. Kant claims that we cannot devalue humanity by treating people without the respect they deserve.

These two formulas for morality provide valuable ethical guidance for deliberation. The first formulation reminds us to consider others and not to make exceptions of ourselves. For example, if I do not want someone to lie to me, then I should not lie to anyone. This formula creates a standard of consistency for moral thinking. The second formulation places limits on our conduct and reminds us that we must respect the welfare of all people. For example, I cannot use someone merely as a means to get what I want; doing so belittles individuals and thwarts their autonomy. This formula reminds us that our actions can affect people and that we must consider the lives of others. Indeed, Deontology provides a way of thinking about the intentions that motivate action, stresses the importance of respecting people, and encourages us to pursue right acts for the sake of morality.

Virtue Ethics

Virtue ethics traces its history to ancient Greek philosophy. Over 2,500 years ago, Aristotle (384–322 BCE) wrote *Nicomachean Ethics*, the first ethical treatise. He constructed one of the most comprehensive accounts of virtue ethics. In his book, he gives the reader a guide to living well and describes what we need to do to become virtuous.

Unlike Kant's and Mill's principle-driven theories, Aristotle's virtue ethics stresses the importance of character. How we act, Aristotle notes, affects how we live, and activity is essential to the cultivation of moral character. He claims that we should deliberately think about our choices and actions because our actions, especially habitual actions, influence and mold our character. Over time, habits form, and we must take care to avoid habits that are harmful—even vicious.

Aristotle begins with the claim that all human actions aim at something good, and happiness is the ultimate good. The purpose of morality, Aristotle explains, is to help us learn to be good so that we can live well. When we are good, we can flourish and achieve happiness. Aristotle's approach to ethics draws upon his view that people can learn virtue which is the path to happiness. He does not believe that people are born good or bad but rather that people are born with the capacity to be rational. In other words, we are responsible for our characters, and we can choose who we become.

Aristotle describes two types of virtue, intellectual and moral. Intellectual virtues, he claims, are acquired through education. They help us to reason well. Moral virtues, in contrast, are developed through practice and habit. They enable us to act well.

Virtues, as we have seen, consists of two kinds, intellectual virtue and moral virtue. Intellectual virtue or excellence owes its origin and development chiefly to teaching, and for that reason requires experience and time. Moral virtue, on the other hand, is formed by habit [...] This shows, too, that none of the moral virtues is implanted in us by nature, for nothing which exists by nature can be changed by habit. For example, it is impossible for a stone, which has a natural downward movement, to become habituated to moving upward, even if one should try ten thousand times to inculcate the habit by throwing it in the air; nor can fire be made to move downward, nor can the direction of any nature-given tendency be changed by habituation. Thus, the virtues are implanted in us neither by nature nor contrary to nature: we are by nature equipped with the ability to receive them, and habit brings this ability to completion and fulfillment.[9]

Over time, our actions form into patterns of behavior that manifest our character. A virtue is a good character trait whereas a vice is a bad character trait. The virtues are valuable because they help us to live well and benefit others; the vices do neither. Learning to live well takes practice and consistency. Cultivating the virtues is essential to a good life.

For Aristotle, the virtues are not extremes. They are balanced and fall within the mean, which is his mark of excellence. For example, Aristotle describes the virtues of courage and generosity and how these virtues never reach the heights of excess or the lows of deficiency. Courage resides between the extremes of cowardice and recklessness. Generosity exists between the extremes of stinginess and extravagance. In this regard, Aristotle explains how the virtuous person understands the moral dimensions of a situation and makes good judgments.

Our discussion has sufficiently established (1) that moral virtue is a mean and in what sense it is a mean; (2) that it is a mean between two vices one of which is marked by excess and the other deficiency; and (3) that it is a mean in the sense that it aims at the median in the emotions and in actions. That is why it is a hard task to be good; in every case it is a task to find the median; for instance, not everyone can find the middle of a circle, but only a man who has the proper knowledge. Similarly, anyone can get angry—that is easy—or can give away money or spend it; but to do all this to the right person, to the right extent, at the right time, for the right reason, and in the right way is no longer something easy that anyone can do. It is for this reason that good conduct is rare, praiseworthy, and noble.[10]

---

[9] Aristotle, *Nicomachean Ethics*. Translated by Martin Ostwald (New Jersey: Prentice Hall, 1999), 33 [1103a14–25].
[10] Aristotle, *Nicomachean Ethics*, 49–50 [1109a19–30].

Aristotle claims that we become virtuous through virtuous activity and describes how the cultivation of such tendencies requires knowledge. People must know what they are doing; they must have the relevant knowledge and understand how to apply it in the situation. Character formation involves hard work, and moral choice requires the ability to assess the circumstances.

Virtue ethics provides a valuable framework for asking what kind of person we want to be and for guiding our deliberations about moral conflicts. Instead of stressing general rules of conduct, Aristotle describes how morality requires a sensitivity to and awareness of individual circumstances. For example, in the 1950s, Dr. Martin Luther King, Jr. engaged in a campaign of nonviolent resistance to champion American civil rights and to advance racial equality. Many of his crusades, such as the Montgomery Bus Boycott of 1955, were in violation of US segregation laws. To claim, however, that Dr. King's actions were merely a breach of law is inadequate. We must also acknowledge his moral character. Dr. King's actions reflect the goodness of his character and his devotion to ideals of justice. Thus, an understanding of his conduct must go beyond formulas and principles and recognize his virtuous character.

By incorporating the methods of Virtue Ethics in moral deliberation, we can see an alternative approach to morality that differs from theories like Utilitarianism and Deontology that rely on overarching principles. Because the world is complex and diverse, morality cannot be strictly uniform, invariable, or formulaic. Recall the example of Dr. King. He shows us that, in order to do the right thing, sometimes we must defy the rules. Virtue Ethics encourages us to avoid short-sightedness and impetuosity. It emphasizes developing our capacities as responsible agents and of comprehending the distinctiveness of each situation. An ethics of character calls us to evaluate who we are as moral beings.

Summary

The three approaches to ethics are different, but each provides useful direction as we navigate the real world. Utilitarianism, Deontology, and Virtue Ethics supply us with strategies that highlight our moral commitments and equip us with methods for deliberation. A Utilitarian model of deliberation provides clear practical guidance. By calculating benefits and risks, we can effectively prioritize everyone's interests and stress the importance of community. On this model, we factor the potential for human suffering into our moral calculus and recognize both positive and negative impacts on society. Deontology, another principled approach to morality, privileges duty and offers a framework for identifying universal moral rules that are both objective and impartial. This structure supports consistency and respect for persons. Finally, Virtue Ethics centers on the importance of character and interprets behavior in relation to individual circumstances. This approach to morality is beneficial for deliberation because it enables us to recognize the uniqueness of every situation and to empathetically support difference.

In combination, these three classical theories promote critical methodologies for deliberation. Utilitarianism and Deontology can help to guide action, and Virtue Ethics can encourage sensitivity to the moral complexities of individual situations. Working together, each theory reinforces the importance of our moral commitments and highlights their interconnectedness.

Cultivating ethical thinking habits is, indeed, a learning experience. The ability to recognize and resolve conflicts takes practice, but the ramifications of inconsistent ethical thinking can be profound. By developing effective reasoning practices, we can learn how to respond judiciously and with integrity.

References

Aristotle. *Nicomachean Ethics*. Translated by Martin Ostwald. New Jersey: Prentice Hall, 1999.

Kant, Immanuel. *The Cambridge Edition of the Works of Immanuel Kant: Practical Philosophy*. Translated and edited by Mary J. Gregor. New York: Cambridge University Press, 1996.

Mill, John Stuart. *Utilitarianism*, 2nd ed. Edited by George Sher. Indianapolis: Hackett Publishing Company, Inc., 2001.

Selections from "Why Care About Caring?"

Nel Noddings

The main task in this chapter is a preliminary analysis of caring. I want to ask what it means to care and to lay down the lines along which analysis will proceed in chapters two and three. It seems obvious in an everyday sense why we should be interested in caring. Everywhere we hear the complaint "Nobody cares!" and our increasing immersion in bureaucratic procedures and regulations leads us to predict that the complaint will continue to be heard. As human beings we want to care and to be cared for. *Caring* is important in itself. It seems necessary, however, to motivate the sort of detailed analysis I propose; that is, it is reasonable in a philosophical context to ask: Why care about caring?

If we were starting out on a traditional investigation of what it means to be moral, we would almost certainly start with a discussion of moral judgment and moral reasoning. This approach has obvious advantages. It gives us something public and tangible to grapple with—the statements that describe our thinking on moral matters. But I shall argue that this is not the only—nor even the best—starting point. Starting the discussion of moral matters with principles, definitions, and demonstrations is rather like starting the solution of a mathematical problem formally. Sometimes we can and do proceed this way, but when the problematic situation is new, baffling, or especially complex, we cannot start this way. We have to operate in an intuitive or receptive mode that is somewhat mysterious, internal, and nonsequential. After the solution has been found by intuitive methods, we may proceed with the construction of a formal demonstration or proof. As the mathematician Gauss put it: "I have got my result but I do not know yet how to get (prove) it."[1]

A difficulty in mathematics teaching is that we too rarely share our fundamental mathematical thinking with our students. We present everything ready-made as it were, as though it springs from our foreheads in formal perfection. The same sort of difficulty arises when we approach the teaching of morality or ethical behavior from a rational-cognitive approach. We fail to share with each other the feelings, the conflicts, the hopes and ideas that influence our eventual choices. We share only the justification for our acts and not what motivates and touches us.

---

[1] Gauss's remark is quoted by Morris Kline, *Why Johnny Can't Add* (New York: Vintage Books, 1974), p. 58.

I think we are doubly mistaken when we approach moral matters in this mathematical way. First, of course, we miss sharing the heuristic processes in our ethical thinking just as we miss that sharing when we approach mathematics itself formally. But this difficulty could be remedied pedagogically. We would not have to change our approach to ethics but only to the teaching of ethical behavior or ethical thinking. Second, however, when we approach moral matters through the study of moral reasoning, we are led quite naturally to suppose that ethics is necessarily a subject that must be cast in the language of principle and demonstration. This, I shall argue, is a mistake.

Many persons who live moral lives do not approach moral problems formally. Women, in particular, seem to approach moral problems by placing themselves as nearly as possible in concrete situations and assuming personal responsibility for the choices to be made. They define themselves in terms of *caring* and work their way through moral problems from the position of one-caring.[2] This position or attitude of caring activates a complex structure of memories, feelings, and capacities. Further, the process of moral decision making that is founded on caring requires a process of concretization rather than one of abstraction. An ethic built on caring is, I think, characteristically and essentially feminine—which is not to say, of course, that it cannot be shared by men, any more than we should care to say that traditional moral systems cannot be embraced by women. But an ethic of caring arises, I believe, out of our experience as women, just as the traditional logical approach to ethical problems arises more obviously from masculine experience.

One reason, then, for conducting the comprehensive and appreciative investigation of caring to which we shall now turn is to capture conceptually a feminine—or simply an alternative—approach to matters of morality.

What Does it Mean To Care?

Our dictionaries tell us that "care" is a state of mental suffering or of engrossment: to care is to be in a burdened mental state, one of anxiety, fear, or solicitude about something or someone. Alternatively, one cares for something or someone if one has a regard for or inclination toward that something or someone. If I have an inclination toward mathematics, I may willingly spend some time with it, and if I have a regard for you, what you think, feel, and desire will matter to me. And, again, to care may mean to be charged with the protection, welfare, or maintenance of something or someone.

These definitions represent different uses of "care" but, in the deepest human sense, we shall see that elements of each of them are involved in caring. In one sense, I may equate "cares" with "burdens"; I have cares in certain matters (professional, personal, or public) if I have burdens or worries, if I fret

---

[2] See Carol Gilligan, "In a Different Voice: Women's Conception of the Self and of Morality," *Harvard Educational Review* 47 (1977), 481–517. Also, "Women's Place in Man's Life Cycle," *Harvard Educational Review* 49 (1979), 431–466. Also, *In a Different Voice* (Cambridge, Mass.: Harvard University Press), 1982.

over current and projected states of affairs. In another sense, I *care* for someone if I feel a stir of desire or inclination toward him. In a related sense, I *care* for someone if I have regard for his views and interests. In the third sense, I have the care of an elderly relative if I am charged with the responsibility for his physical welfare. But, clearly, in the deep human sense that will occupy us, I cannot claim to care for my relative if my caretaking is perfunctory or grudging.

We see that it will be necessary to give much of our attention to the one-caring in our analysis. Even though we sometimes judge caring from the outside, as third-persons, it is easy to see that the essential elements of caring are located in the relation between the one-caring and the cared-for. In a lovely little book, *On Caring*, Milton Mayeroff describes caring largely through the view of one-caring. He begins by saying: "To care for another person, in the most significant sense, is to help him grow and actualize himself."[3]

I want to approach the problem a bit differently, because I think emphasis on the actualization of the other may lead us to pass too rapidly over the description of what goes on in the one-caring. Further, problems arise in the discussion of reciprocity, and we shall feel a need to examine the role of the cared-for much more closely also. But Mayeroff has given us a significant start by pointing to the importance of constancy, guilt, reciprocation, and the limits of caring. All of these we shall consider in some detail.

Let's start looking at caring from the outside to discover the limitations of that approach. In the ordinary course of events, we expect some action from one who claims to care, even though action is not all we expect. How are we to determine whether Mr. Smith cares for his elderly mother, who is confined to a nursing home? It is not enough, surely, that Mr. Smith should say, "I care." (But the possibility of his saying this will lead us onto another path of analysis shortly. We shall have to examine caring from the inside.) We, as observers, must look for some action, some manifestation in Smith's behavior, that will allow us to agree that he cares. To care, we feel, requires some action in behalf of the cared-for. Thus, if Smith never visits his mother, nor writes to her, nor telephones her, we would be likely to say that, although he is charged formally with her care—he pays for her confinement—he does not really care. We point out that he seems to be lacking in regard, that he is not troubled enough to see for himself how his mother fares. There is no desire for her company, no inclination toward her. But notice that a criterion of action would not be easy to formulate from this case. Smith, after all, does perform some action in behalf of his mother: he pays for her physical maintenance. But we are looking for a qualitatively different sort of action.

Is direct, externally observable action necessary to caring? Can caring be present in the absence of action in behalf of the cared-for? Consider the problem of lovers who cannot marry because they are already committed to satisfactory and honorable marriages. The lover learns that his beloved is ill. All his instincts cry out for his presence at her bedside. Yet, if he fears for the trouble he may bring her, for the recriminations that may spring from his appearance, he may stay away from her. Surely,

---

[3] Milton Mayeroff, *On Caring* (New York: Harper and Row, 1971), p. 1.

we would not say in such a case that the lover does not care. He is in a mental state of engrossment, even suffering; he feels the deepest regard and, charged by his love with the duty to protect, he denies his own need in order to spare her one form of pain. Thus, in caring, he chooses not to act directly and tenderly in response to the beloved's immediate physical pain. We see that, when we consider the action component of caring in depth, we shall have to look beyond observable action to acts of commitment, those acts that are seen only by the individual subject performing them.

In the case of the lover whose beloved has fallen ill, we might expect him to express himself when the crisis has passed. But even this might not happen. He might resolve never to contact her again, and his caring could then be known only to him as he renews his resolve again and again. We do not wish to deny that the lover cares, but clearly, something is missing in the relationship: caring is not completed in the cared-for. Or, consider the mother whose son, in young adulthood, leaves home in anger and rebellion. Should she act to bring about reconciliation? Perhaps. Are we sure that she does not care if she fails to act directly to bring him into loving contact with his family? She may, indeed, deliberately abstain from acting in the belief that her son must be allowed to work out his problem alone. Her regard for him may force her into anguished and carefully considered inaction. Like the lover, she may eventually express herself to her son—when the crisis has passed—but then again, she may not. After a period of, say, two years, the relationship may stabilize, and the mother's caring may resume its usual form. Shall we say, then, that she "cares again" and that for two years she "did not care"?

There are still further difficulties in trying to formulate an action criterion for caring. Suppose that I learn about a family in great need, and suppose that I decide to help them. I pay their back rent for them, buy food for them, and supply them with the necessities of life. I do all this cheerfully, willingly spending time with them. Can it be doubted that I care? This sort of case will raise problems also. Suppose both husband and wife in this family want to be independent, or at least have a latent longing in this direction. But my acts tend to suppress the urge toward independence. Am I helping or hindering?[4] Do I care or only seem to care? If it must be said that my relation to the needy family is not, properly, a caring relation, what has gone wrong?

Now, in this brief inspection of caring acts, we have already encountered problems. Others suggest themselves. What of indirect caring, for example? What shall we say about college students who engage in protests for the blacks of South Africa or the "boat people" of Indochina or the Jews of Russia? Under what conditions would we be willing to say that they care? Again, these may be questions that can be answered only by those claiming to care. We need to know, for example, what motivates the protest. Then, as we shall see, there is the recurring problem of "completion." How is the caring conveyed to the cared-for? What sort of meeting can there be between the one-caring and the cared-for?

We are not going to be able to answer all of these questions with certainty. Indeed, this essay is not aiming toward a systematic exposition of criteria for caring. Rather, I must show that such a systematic effort is, so far as the system is its goal, mistaken. We expend the effort as much to show what is not

---

[4] See David Brandon, *Zen in the Art of Helping* (New York: Dell Publishing Co., 1978), chap. 3.

fruitful as what is. It is not my aim to be able to sort cases at the finish: A cares, B does not care, C cares but not about D, etc. If we can understand how complex and intricate, indeed how subjective, caring is, we shall perhaps be better equipped to meet the conflicts and pains it sometimes induces. Then, too, we may come to understand at least in part how it is that, in a country that spends billions on caretaking of various sorts, we hear everywhere the complaint, "Nobody cares."

In spite of the difficulties involved, we shall have to discuss behavioral indicators of caring in some depth, because we will be concerned about problems of entrusting care, of monitoring caretaking and assigning it. When we consider the possibility of institutional caring and what might be meant by the "caring school," we shall need to know what to look for. And so, even though the analysis will move us more and more toward first- and second-person views of caring, we shall examine caring acts and the "third-person" view also. In this initial analysis, we shall return to the third-person view after examining first- and second-person aspects.

So far, we have talked about the action component of caring, and we certainly have not arrived at a determinate set of criteria. Suppose, now, that we consider the engrossment we expect to find in the one-caring, When Mr. Smith, whose "caring" seems to us to be at best perfunctory, says, "I care," what can he mean? Now, clearly we can only guess, because Mr. Smith has to speak for himself on this. But he might mean: (1) I *do* care. I think of my mother often and worry about her. It is an awful burden. (2) I *do* care. I should see her more often, but I have so much to do—a houseful of kids, long working hours, a wife who needs my companionship.... (3) I do care. I pay the bills, don't I? I have sisters who could provide company....

These suggested meanings do not exhaust Mr. Smith's possibilities, but they give us something to work with. In the first case, we might rightly conclude that Mr. Smith does not care for his mother as much as he docs for himself as caretaker. He is burdened with cares, and the focus of his attention has shifted inward to himself and his worries. This, we shall see, is a risk of caring. There exists in all caring situations the risk that the one-caring will be overwhelmed by the responsibilities and duties of the task and that, as a result of being burdened, he or she will cease to care for the other and become instead the object of "caring." Now, here—and throughout our discussion on caring—we must try to avoid equivocation. There are, as we have noted, several common meanings of "to care," but no one of them yields the deep sense for which we are probing. When it is dear that "caring" refers to one of the restricted senses, or when we are not yet sure to what it refers, I shall enclose it in quotes. In the situation where Mr. Smith is *burdened with cares*, he is the object of "caring."

In the third case, also, we might justifiably conclude that Mr. Smith does not care. His interest is in equity. He wants to be credited with caring. By doing something, he hopes to find an acceptable substitute for genuine caring. We see similar behavior in the woman who professes to love animals and whisks every stray to the animal shelter. Most animals, once at the shelter, suffer death. Does one who cares choose swift and merciful death for the object of her care over precarious and perhaps painful life? Well, we might say, it depends. It depends on our caretaking capabilities, on traffic conditions where we live, on the physical condition of the animal. All this is exactly to the point. What we do depends not upon rules, or at least not wholly on rules—not upon a prior determination of what is fair or equitable—but upon a constellation of conditions that is viewed through both the eyes of the one-caring and the eyes of the cared-for. By and large, we do not say with any conviction that a person cares if that person acts routinely according to some fixed rule.

The second case is difficult. This Mr. Smith has a notion that caring involves a commitment of self, but he is finding it difficult to handle the commitments he has already made. He is in conflict over how he should spend himself. Undergoing conflict is another risk of caring, and we shall consider a variety of possible conflicts. Of special interest to us will be the question: When should I attempt to remove conflict, and when should I resolve simply to Live with the conflict? Suppose, for example, that I care for both cats and birds. (I must use "care for" at this stage without attempting to justify its use completely.) Having particular cats of my own and *not* having particular birds of my own at the same time are indications of my concern for each. But there are wild birds in my garden, and they are in peril from the cats. I may give the matter considerable thought. I feed the cats well so that they will not hunt out of hunger. I hang small bells on their collars. I keep bird cages ready for victims I am able to rescue. I keep bird baths and feeders inaccessible to the cats. Beyond this, I live with the conflict. Others might have the cats declawed, but I will not do this. Now, the point here is not whether I care more for cats than birds, or whether Ms. Jones (who declaws her cats) cares more for birds than I do. The point lies in trying to discern the kinds of things I must think about when I am in a conflict of caring. When my caring is directed to living things, I must consider their natures, ways of life, needs, and desires. And, although I can never accomplish it entirely, I try to apprehend the reality of the other.

This is the fundamental aspect of caring from the inside. When I look at and think about how I am when I care, I realize that there is invariably this displacement of interest from my own reality to the reality of the other. (Our discussion now will be confined to caring for persons,) Kierkegaard has said that we apprehend another's reality as *possibility*.[5] To be touched, to have aroused in me something that will disturb my own ethical reality, I must see the other's reality as a possibility for my own. This is not to say that I cannot try to see the other's reality differently, Indeed, I can. I can look at it objectively by collecting factual data; I can look at it historically. If it is heroic, I can come to admire it. But this sort of looking does not touch my own ethical reality; it may even distract me from it. As Kierkegaard put it:

> Ethically speaking there is nothing so conducive to sound sleep as admiration of another person's ethical reality. And again ethically speaking, if there is anything that can stir and rouse a man. it is a possibility ideally requiring itself of a human being.[6]

---

[5] Søren Kierkegaard, *Concluding Unscientific Postscript,* trans. David F. Swenson and Walter Lowrie (Princeton: Princeton University Press, 1941).
[6] Ibid., p.322.

But I am suggesting that we do not see only the direct possibilities for becoming better than we are when we struggle toward the reality of the other. We also have aroused in us the feeling, "I must do something." When we see the other's reality as a possibility for us, we must act to eliminate the intolerable, to reduce the pain, to fill the need, to actualize the dream. When I am in this sort of relationship with another, when the other's reality becomes a real possibility for me, I care. Whether the caring is sustained, whether it lasts long enough to be conveyed to the other, whether it becomes visible in the world, depends upon my sustaining the relationship or, at least, acting out of concern for my own ethicality as though it were sustained.

In this latter case, one in which something has slipped away from me or eluded me from the start but in which I strive to regain or to attain it, I experience a genuine caring for self. This caring for self, for the *ethical* self, can emerge only from a caring for others. But a sense of my physical self, a knowledge of what gives me pain and pleasure, precedes my caring for others. Otherwise, their realities as possibilities for my own reality would mean nothing to me. When we say of someone, "He cares only for himself," we mean that, in our deepest sense, he does not care at all. He has only a sense of that physical self—of what gives him pain and pleasure. Whatever he sees in others is pre-selected in relation to his own needs and desires. He does not see the reality of the other as a possibility for himself but only as an instance of what he has already determined as self or not-self. Thus, he is ethically both zero and finished. His only "becoming" is a physical becoming. It is clear, of course, that I must say more about what is meant by "ethical reality" and "ethical self," and I shall return to this question.

I need not, however, be a person who cares only for myself in order to behave occasionally as though I care only for myself. Sometimes I behave this way because I have not thought through things carefully enough and because the mode of the times pushes the thoughtless in its own direction. Suppose, for example, that I am a teacher who loves mathematics. I encounter a student who is doing poorly, and I decide to have a talk with him. He tells me that he hates mathematics. *Aha*, I think. *Here is the problem. I must help this poor boy to love mathematics, and then he will do better at it.* What am I doing when I proceed in this way? I am not trying to grasp the reality of the other as a possibility for myself. I have not even asked: *How would it feel to hate mathematics?* Instead, I project my own reality onto my student and say, *You will be just fine if only you learn to love mathematics.* And I have "data" to support me. There is evidence that intrinsic motivation is associated with higher achievement. (Did anyone ever doubt this?) So my student becomes an object of study and manipulation for me. Now, I have deliberately chosen an example that is not often associated with manipulation. Usually, we associate manipulation with trying to get our student to achieve some learning objective that we have devised and set for him. Bringing him to "love mathematics" is seen as a noble aim. And so it is, if it is held out to him as a possibility that he glimpses by observing me and others; but then I shall not be disappointed in him, or in myself, if he remains indifferent to mathematics. It is a possibility that may not be actualized. What matters to me, if I care, is that he find some reason, acceptable in his inner self, for learning the mathematics required of him or that he reject it boldly and honestly.

How would it feel to hate mathematics? What reasons could I find for learning it? When I think this way, I refuse to cast about for rewards that might pull him along. He must find his rewards. I do not begin with dazzling performances designed to intrigue him or to change his attitude. I begin, as nearly as I can, with the view from his eyes: Mathematics is bleak, jumbled, scary, boring, boring, boring.... What in the world could induce me to engage in it? From that point on, we struggle together with it.

Apprehending the other's reality, feeling what he feels as nearly as possible, is the essential part of caring from the view of the one-caring. For if I take on the other's reality as possibility and begin to feel its reality, I feel, also, that I must act accordingly; that is, I am impelled to act as though in my own behalf, but in behalf of the other. Now, of course, this feeling that I must act may or may not be sustained, I must make a commitment to act. The commitment to act in behalf of the cared-for, a continued interest in his reality throughout the appropriate time span, and the continual renewal of commitment over this span of time are the essential elements of caring from the inner view. Mayeroff speaks of devotion and the promotion of growth in the cared-for. I wish to start with engrossment and motivational displacement. Both concepts will require elaboration. [...]

The Moral Pillars of Biomedical Ethics

By Katherine K. Johnson

Introduction

Ethical controversies in healthcare often involve moral questions that have no easy answers. Bioethics attempts to address these questions; it is a branch of applied philosophy that examines practical questions about issues in healthcare, medicine, and research. Bioethics is a unique field of study because unlike other philosophical subjects, it navigates real-life scenarios that require actual solutions.

Moral principles are an indispensable part of ethical decision-making. The basic principles of biomedical ethics constitute the moral foundation of healthcare. They provide a framework for ethical decision-making and conflict resolution. Beneficence, nonmaleficence, respect for autonomy, and justice are the four moral pillars.[1]

These principles of biomedical ethics codify the standards for right action, yet, they are not absolute. They allow for nuance and exceptions. These pillars are best translated as *prima facie* norms of conduct that offer a scaffolding for moral deliberation. While they impose binding obligations, they also permit us to choose which principle best fits a particular situation when duties collide.[2] In other words, *prima facie* principles express our apparent moral duties but also acknowledge frequent conflicts. For example, sometimes the best way to promote patients' best interests may cause them some pain.

In this [reading], I present an overview of the four principles, convey their meaning and scope, and highlight their corresponding duties. I also provide historical examples of each of the pillars and discuss the complexities of these cases. These four norms of conduct were developed primarily to benefit patients, but they also systematize the responsibilities of clinicians and researchers. They fulfill the obligations of the healthcare worker and promote the public's trust. These principles identify a common moral language and the shared interprofessional values for all individuals who work together in the healthcare environment.

---

[1] One of the most comprehensive accounts of the principles of biomedical ethics is written by Beauchamp and Childress. I draw heavily on their descriptions of the four principles. See Tom L. Beauchamp and James F. Childress, *Principles of Biomedical Ethics*, 6th ed. (New York: Oxford University Press, 2009).

[2] For an account of *prima facie* principles, see W. D. Ross, *The Right and the Good* (New York: Oxford University Press, 2002).

Beneficence

Beneficence, the first principle of biomedical ethics, codifies a clear prescription to benefit patients.[3] This standard imposes a positive obligation on providers to advance the well-being of patients and defends the duty to maximize goods and benefits and to remove harms and burdens. It expresses the central obligation of healthcare workers: to determine what most benefits their patients.

Beneficence prompts individuals to *actively* promote the good and minimize disadvantages and risks. For example, healthcare providers must dynamically work to improve the human condition by restoring health and eradicating harms like illness and disease. As a principle of right action, beneficence demands that we advance the welfare of others and conscientiously prevent harm.

The history of beneficence in bioethics begins with a demand for ethical research standards after the atrocities inflicted by Nazi scientists on prisoners of the Holocaust during World War II. The Nuremburg Code (1947), one of the first documents that organized ethical standards of research, arises out of the Nuremburg war trials at the end of WWII. Another advance in the development of ethical standards in research resulted from a 1972 report disclosing crimes perpetrated by American scientists in the Tuskegee Syphilis Study. Following this report, President Richard Nixon signed the National Research Act of 1974 into law. This law created the National Commission for the Protection of Human Subjects in Biomedical and Behavioral Research.

In 1979, the National Commission published *The Belmont Report* in response to a need for greater research protections. This crucial document codifies three broad standards for the ethical treatment of human subjects in research: beneficence, respect for persons, and justice. The report describes beneficence as:

> Persons are treated in an ethical manner not only by respecting their decisions and protecting them from harm, but also by making efforts to secure their well-being. Such treatment falls under the principle of beneficence. The term "beneficence" is often understood to cover acts of kindness or charity that go beyond strict obligation. In this document, beneficence is understood, in a stronger sense, as an obligation. Two general rules have been formulated as complementary expressions of beneficent actions in this sense: (1) do no harm and (2) maximize possible benefits and minimize possible harms.[4]

The duty of beneficence requires that clinicians recognize and promote their patients' best interests and actively prevent harm. Consider a case from 2002 that touches on issues of not only beneficence but also potential child abuse and ableism. Ashley X was born with profound cognitive and developmental

---

[3] Beauchamp and Childress, *Principles of Biomedical Ethics*, 197–239.

[4] The National Commission for the Protection of Human Subjects of Biomedical and Behavioral Research, The Belmont Report, 1979, https://www.hhs.gov/ohrp/regulations-and-policy/belmont-report/index.html.

disabilities.[5] At the age of six, Ashley began to show signs of early puberty and accelerated growth. Her parents became concerned that they would no longer be able to care for their daughter as she grew bigger. Ashley's parents and her physicians, therefore, constructed a plan to temper her growth. Ashley received estrogen treatments, a hysterectomy, and removal of her breast buds. According to the family, these "growth-attenuating" procedures were meant to benefit the child. After nearly three years of surgeries and hormone treatments, Ashley reached her final height of 4'6" and a weight of 65 lbs.[6] Did the nonmedically necessary interventions benefit the patient or the family? How should we interpret this case in the context of beneficence?

The case of Ashley X, indeed, highlights the challenges of implementing beneficence. On the one hand, if Ashley remained "forever small," she could stay at home and be cared for by her family. Her parents loved their daughter and wanted to continue to care for her.[7] If Ashley continued to grow, she would have likely had to move out of the family home and be cared for by others with less interest in her welfare. From this standpoint, the motives of all involved—parents and physicians—were benevolent; they had the best interests and well-being of Ashley in mind. On the other hand, however, nonmedically necessary surgeries and treatments still come with risks. Even the best wishes of the family and doctors cannot justify acts that disregard medically beneficial care. The principle of beneficence requires that providers actively promote the good and minimize harm. In the case of Ashley X, different benefits and risks are in conflict. How they are balanced in this problematic situation is crucial.

Nonmaleficence

Nonmaleficence, the second principle of biomedical ethics, articulates a clear limit on conduct to avoid causing harm.[8] This principle is different than beneficence because it imposes a negative obligation; healthcare workers must avoid acting in ways that may cause harm or the risk of harm. In other words, nonmaleficence places limits on what clinicians can do. The duty to do no harm is negative and does not require the active removal of disadvantages. Instead, nonmaleficence directs providers to be cautious and sensitive to risk.

Nonmaleficence's prescriptions align with standards of due care. Both demand a decent minimum of competent care. Philosopher Tom Beauchamp and theologian James Childress sum up the connection.

> Obligations of nonmaleficence include not only obligations not to inflict harms, but also obligations not to impose risks of harm. A person can harm or place

---

[5] Daniel F. Gunther and Douglas S. Diekema, "Attenuating Growth in Children with Profound Developmental Disabilities: A New Approach to an Old Dilemma," *The Archives of Pediatrics & Adolescent Medicine* 160 (2006): 1013–1017; Eva Feder Kittay, "Forever Small: The Strange Case of Ashley X," *Hypatia* 26 (2011): 610–631; Douglas S. Diekema and Norman Fost. "Ashley Revisited: A Response to the Critics." *The American Journal of Bioethics* 10 (2010): 30–44.

[6] Diekema and Fost, "Ashley Revisited," 31.

[7] Kittay's classification of Ashley's treatment, as titled in her article, "Forever Small: The Strange Case of Ashley X."

[8] Beauchamp and Childress, *Principles of Biomedical Ethics*, 149–196.

another person at risk without malicious or harmful intent, and the agent of harm may or may not be morally or legally responsible for the harms. [...] In cases of risk imposition, both law and morality recognize a standard of due care that determines whether the agent who is causally responsible for the risk is legally or morally responsible as well. This standard is a specification of the principle of nonmaleficence. Due care is taking sufficient and appropriate care to avoid causing harm, as the circumstances demand of a reasonable and prudent person.[9]

The principle of nonmaleficence illuminates the importance of risk assessment when communicating information to patients. Providers must avoid discussing uncertain treatments with dubious efficacy that may be hazardous to patients.

As an example of nonmaleficence, let us examine the case of Theresa Ann Campo Pearson.[10] In Florida in 1992, Theresa Pearson was born with anencephaly, a serious birth defect and genetic disorder in which parts of the brain and skull do not develop. This condition is terminal. Theresa, the doctors and family knew, would live no more than a few days.

Theresa's case sparked public outrage when media outlets reported that her parents had made the unusual decision to terminate her life in order to donate her organs to those in need of a transplant.[11] The parent's wishes, however, conflicted with Florida state law. Florida law allows living persons to donate organs but prohibits killing people for the sake of harvesting their organs. In the words of circuit judge Estella M. Moriarty, "doctors can take as many transplant organs as possible from the terminally ill 6-day-old infant as long as they don't kill her in the process" and "I can't authorize someone to take your baby's life, however short, however unsatisfactory, to save another child."[12]

Clearly, nonmaleficence bears upon this case. Is the obligation to do no harm best understood as safeguarding biological life?

While Florida state law views nonmaleficence as a prohibition against taking a life, some bioethicists argue that the baby, even though she was breathing and her heart was beating, was essentially dead given her terminal condition. She was unable to experience life in any meaningful way. To end baby Theresa's life early, scholars argued, is not a violation of the principle of nonmaleficence. Failure to save viable organs, however, can be viewed as a breach of this obligation. Further, from this standpoint, failing to follow the parent's wishes may have allowed the child to suffer at the expense of an antiquated

---

[9] Beauchamp and Childress, Principles of Biomedical Ethics, 153.

[10] James Rachels, *The Elements of Moral Philosophy*, 8th ed. (New York: McGraw Hill, 2015); Piotr Szawarski and John Oram, "Classic Cases Revisited: Baby Theresa and the Definition of Death." *Journal of the Intensive Care Society* 16 (2015): 222–225; Gina Kolata, "Malformed Infant's Brief Life Forces an Issue of Medical Ethics," The *New York Times*, April 5, 1991, https://www.nytimes.com/1991/04/05/weekinreview/the-nation-a-malformed-infant-s-brief-life-forces-an-issue-of-medical-ethics.html.

[11] Rachels, *The Elements of Moral Philosophy*, 1–6; Szawarski, and Oram, "*Classic Cases Revisited*," 222.

[12] Szawarski and Oram, "*Classic Cases Revisited*," 222.

notion of death and assumptions about the nature of harm.[13] Clearly, nonmaleficence, like all the principles, remains difficult to apply in real-world situations.

Respect for Autonomy

Respect for autonomy, the third principle of biomedical ethics, honors the self-governing and decision-making capacities of rational people.[14] Autonomy draws from the ideal that people should be free to make their own decisions without coercion by others. In healthcare, autonomous people, those patients capable of making decisions and acting upon them, should be allowed to exercise their capacity for self-determination. They should be able to choose their own paths in life.

Sometimes, a competent person may struggle to make an autonomous choice regarding their healthcare needs. Incomplete or ambiguous information can impair a rational person from making a decision that aligns with their values and goals. Indeed, medical information is complex, and sick patients often struggle to make decisions in stressful situations. Patients need help to assess and evaluate information.

Autonomy imposes both positive and negative obligations on healthcare workers. Positively, providers have a duty to assist patients in their decision-making. For example, healthcare workers must help patients interpret, navigate, and understand complex medical information. Negatively, clinicians have a duty not to interfere in a patient's agency. For example, providers must not withhold facts about a case or prognosis; they must provide accurate and truthful information.

Like beneficence and nonmaleficence, autonomy is not an absolute moral command. Rather, it is a *prima facie* principle that articulates a duty to honor people's rational choices. However, sometimes choices can be irrational or harmful. Providers are not required to honor every patient request, and sometimes patient autonomy must be curtailed to protect an individual or others from harm. For example, if patients are sick with a dangerous and highly transmissible illness, they can be quarantined against their wills. While this action may appear a violation of autonomy, individual choices cannot infringe upon or threaten the well-being of others. Autonomy protects one's right to choose, but it can be justifiably overridden if choices threaten to harm others.

The story of Brittany Maynard illustrates the challenge of autonomy. In 2013, the 28-year-old Californian was diagnosed with terminal brain cancer. Physicians informed her that despite treatment the cancer was spreading and that painful side effects from the tumor would soon fill the remainder of her life. Brittany decided that she wanted to die with dignity. While competent to make her own decisions, Brittany's physicians would not honor her request to die because it was a violation of state law. In California, voluntary euthanasia was illegal. Brittany moved to Oregon and, after the required residency period, peacefully ended her life in 2014.[15]

---

[13] Szawarski and Oram, "*Classic Cases Revisited*," 223–225.

[14] Beauchamp and Childress, *Principles of Biomedical Ethics*, 99–148.

[15] https://deathwithdignity.org/news/2019/11/brittany-maynards-legacy-five-years-on/; https://www.npr.org/sections/thetwo-way/2014/11/03/361094919/as-planned-right-to-die-advocate-brittany-maynard-ends-her-life.

Despite this conclusion to the story, some degree of moral ambiguity about the situation remains. What are the bounds of autonomy? Some ethicists argue that a person's decision to die can be rational even if it appears a harmful act. In contrast, others claim that to choose death is irrational, and healthcare providers cannot be asked to fulfill a patient's wish that is deliberately harmful. As with beneficence and nonmaleficence, respect for autonomy is difficult to navigate in ethically problematic situations, especially those situations that challenge fundamental beliefs about respecting life.

Justice

The principle of justice, the fourth principle of biomedical ethics, concerns the nature of fairness.[16] In healthcare, it applies to the distribution of goods and the fair and equitable treatment of patients. Further, the principle of justice raises questions about the allocation of resources, affordability of treatment, and the availability of care.

Whereas beneficence and nonmaleficence provide rules for producing as much good and avoiding as much harm as possible, justice clarifies how goods and harms should be distributed. Justice articulates the importance of equity in the allocation of advantages and disadvantages. Nonetheless, debates about the nature of justice continue, and its boundaries are not fully established. In the real world, providers must inevitably make choices about resources. Hospitals, for example, have limited supplies, and, as a result, choices are often constrained. Providers must resort to rationing which may not fulfill ideal standards of justice.

Consider the SARS-COVID-2 virus that officially became a pandemic in 2020. As the virus spread from country to country, healthcare systems became overloaded with infected patients. Healthcare organizations were unprepared for the sudden demand. They were ill-equipped to protect both patients and employees from a virus that scientists, at first, knew very little about.

The pandemic fueled the need to ration healthcare resources, from high-filtration N-95 masks for healthcare workers in New York City to ventilators and intensive care beds in Italy.[17] These two locations were hit the hardest early in the pandemic, with skyrocketing transmissibility rates and critically sick and contagious patients. Healthcare workers had to decide on a fair procedure for the allocation of limited resources.

The need to ration raises crucial questions about the nature of justice and its corresponding obligations. Discussing the pandemic crisis, contemporary bioethicist Ezekiel Emanuel proposes four ethical values that can facilitate a judicious distribution of goods.

---

[16] Beauchamp and Childress, *Principles of Biomedical Ethics*, 240–287.

[17] Andrea Lavazza and Mirko D. Garasic, "What If Some Patients are More 'Important' Than Others? A Possible Framework for Covid-19 and Other Emergency Care Situations," *BMC Medical Ethics* 23, 24 (2022): 2–11; Ezekiel J. Emanuel et al., "Fair Allocation of Scarce Medical Resources in the Time of COVID-19," *The New England Journal of Medicine* 382 (May 2020): 2049–2055.

> [M]aximizing benefits, treating equally, promoting and rewarding instrumental value, and giving priority to the worst off—yield six specific recommendations for allocating medical resources in the Covid-19 pandemic: maximize benefits; prioritize health workers; do not allocate on a first-come, first-served basis; be responsive to evidence; recognize research participation; and apply the same principles to all Covid-19 and non-Covid-19 patients.[18]

However efficient and nonbiased these recommendations aim to be, do they adequately reflect the principle of justice? The pandemic shed light on an undeniable, yet, hidden crisis in the healthcare industry, the conflict between individual needs versus the good of society. In Italy, the number of sick patients surpassed the availability of life-saving care. Is it just that many patients could not receive the care they needed to survive?[19] In the US, many cancer patients had to wait for treatment because hospitals were filled with Covid patients. Is it right that people with cancer had to delay necessary medical attention?[20] Individual demand for immediate and critical care surpassed the number of available healthcare workers and supplies to save lives. Healthcare systems struggled to balance the welfare of society with the needs of individual patients. Standards of equity and fairness undoubtedly have a dramatic effect on healthcare practice. The importance of executing a fair and equitable standard of justice in healthcare is undisputed. However, any appeal to justice must confront the reality of exhausted resources and the ability to equip providers with the means to do as much good as they can in a way that maintains standards of fairness, equity, and nondiscrimination.

Summary

Beneficence, nonmaleficence, autonomy, and justice represent the four moral pillars that aim to guide institutional and clinical practice in healthcare. These principles codify the ethical commitments and obligations of healthcare workers and guide both policy and practice. The four pillars assist clinicians, administrators, and researchers in maintaining moral and professional standards of care. These principles support a system that strives toward a fair and equitable use of resources. As supports, they attempt to balance risk and reward, protect individual interests and well-being, and honor the dignity of healthcare vocations.

The Tuskegee Syphilis Study (1932–1972) provides not only an illuminating example of how all four pillars of biomedical ethics can interact and be present,[21] but it is also an example of an egregious

---

[18] Emanuel, "Fair Allocation of Scarce Medical Resources," 2051.

[19] Yascha Mounk, "The Extraordinary Decision Facing Italian Doctors," *The Atlantic*, March 11, 2020.

[20] Rachel Riera et al., "Delays and Disruptions in Cancer Health Care Due to COVID-19 Pandemic: Systematic Review," *JCO Global Oncology: An American Society of Clinical Oncology Journal* 7 (2021): 311–323.

[21] I drew information about the Tuskegee Syphilis Study from the following two sources: Gregory Pence, *Medical Ethics: Accounts of Groundbreaking Cases*, 8th ed. (New York: McGraw-Hill, 2017), 200–209 and Gregory Pence, *The Elements of Bioethics* (New York: McGraw-Hill, 2007), 206–211.

violation of each principle. The US Public Health Service initiated this nontherapeutic study to understand the progress of untreated syphilis. Six hundred poor, black men in Macon County, Alabama, were unwittingly enrolled in the study and were monitored for forty years. Out of the six hundred, nearly four hundred had latent syphilis, but the men were never told that they had the disease and were never informed that they were subjects in a research study run by the US government. When a cure for syphilis was discovered in 1947, the researchers neither informed nor treated participants. The individual and societal outcomes were catastrophic. The untreated disease caused pain and suffering, disfigurement, cognitive damage, and hundreds of deaths. Family members were infected as the disease remained unchecked. The moral failure of the study left a legacy of public distrust in modern medicine in the community.

The study was a failure of all four ethical pillars. First, the study violated beneficence and the basic tenet of patient best interest. It failed to prioritize the well-being of its subjects, and researchers actively caused harm. Moreover, in spite of the forty-year study, no substantial findings about syphilis arose from the research. Second, researchers did not fulfill their obligation to nonmaleficence. When participants sought out other physicians, scientists actively intervened to prevent them from learning about and treating their conditions. They also intentionally exposed participants to risk by subjecting them to spinal taps and other procedures used to collect data. Third, participants' autonomous agency was not respected; in fact, they did not know they were part of a government research study. While informed consent was not a legal requirement for participation in research until 1966, the study was clearly fundamentally flawed as it never informed its subjects *and* actively deceived them in the process.[22] Finally, the study was a clear abuse of justice. In research trials, participants must receive some benefit or at least not be harmed for the sake of the study's goals. The Tuskegee subjects were *not* treated equitably. The study was racist because black men were targeted for the research. The subjects were poor and uneducated, and many were illiterate. Researchers took advantage of their social standing and did so for the sake of their own gain. Justice as fairness is clearly absent in a situation where bias and discrimination dominate actions.

The moral pillars are realistic but are nonetheless difficult to translate in practice because they are often in conflict with our limitations as providers. These principles must be supplemented by objective, yet, empathetic evaluations that prioritize patient values and recognize institutional constraints and bias. The principles of biomedical ethics can only take us so far because they need rational human beings to interpret them in the context of the real world. We must remember that all people are individuals with different histories, values, goals, and conceptions of a good life. When effectively applied, these bioethical standards can promote an environment that is efficient, equitable, and beneficial to both individuals and society. Indeed, healthcare requires moral pillars that promote good habits of cooperation, collaboration, veracity, and respect.

---

[22] Pence, *Medical Ethics,* 206.

References

"Brittany Maynard's Legacy Five Years on." Death with Dignity, November 1, 2019. https://deathwithdignity. org/news/2019/11/brittany-maynards-legacy-five-years-on/.

Beauchamp, Tom L., and James F. Childress. *Principles of Biomedical Ethics*, 6th ed. New York: Oxford University Press, 2009.

Diekema, Douglas S., and Norman Fost. "Ashley Revisited: A Response to the Critics." *The American Journal of Bioethics* 10 (2010): 30–44.

Emanuel, Ezekiel J., Govind Persad, Ross Upshur, Beatriz Thome, Michael Parker, Aaron Glickman, Cathy Zhang, and Connor Boyle, et.al. "Fair Allocation of Scarce Medical Resources in the Time of COVID-19." *The New England Journal of Medicine* 382 (May 2020): 2049–2055.

Gunther, Daniel F., and Douglas S. Diekema. "Attenuating Growth in Children with Profound Developmental Disabilities: A New Approach to an Old Dilemma." *The Archives of Pediatrics & Adolescent Medicine* 160 (2006): 1013–1017.

Jones, James. *Bad Blood*. New York: Free Press, 1981.

Kittay, Eva Feder. "Forever Small: The Strange Case of Ashley X." *Hypatia* 26 (2011): 610–631.

Kolata, Gina. "Malformed Infant's Brief Life Forces an Issue of Medical Ethics." *The New York Times*, April 5, 1991. https://www.nytimes.com/1991/04/05/weekinreview/the-nation-a-malformed-infant-s-brief-life-forces-an-issue-of-medical-ethics.html.

Lavazza, Andrea, and Mirko D. Garasic, "What If Some Patients are More 'Important' Than Others? A Possible Framework for Covid-19 and Other Emergency Care Situations." *BMC Medical Ethics* 23, 24 (2022): 2–11.

Mounk, Yascha. "The Extraordinary Decision Facing Italian Doctors." *The Atlantic*, March 11, 2020. https:// www.theatlantic.com/ideas/archive/2020/03/who-gets-hospital-bed/607807/.

Pence, Gregory. *Medical Ethics: Accounts of Groundbreaking Cases*, 8th ed. New York: McGraw-Hill, 2017.

Pence, Gregory. *Pandemic Bioethics*. Ontario, Canada: Broadview Press, 2021.

Pence, Gregory. *The Elements of Bioethics*. New York: McGraw-Hill, 2007.

Peralta, Eyder. "As Planned, Right-to-Die Advocate Brittany Maynard Ends Her Life." NPR, November 4, 2014. https://www.npr.org/sections/thetwo-way/2014/11/03/361094919/ as-planned-right-to-die-advocate-brittany-maynard-ends-her-life.

Rachels, James. *The Elements of Moral Philosophy*, 8th edition. New York: McGraw-Hill, 2015.

Riera, Rachel, Angela Maria Bagattini, Rafael Leite Pacheco, Daniela Vianna Pachito, Felipe Roitberg, and Andre Ilbawi. "Delays and Disruptions in Cancer Health Care Due to COVID-19 Pandemic: Systematic Review," *JCO Global Oncology: An American Society of Clinical Oncology Journal* 7 (2021): 311–323.

Ross, W. D. *The Right and the Good*. Edited by Philip Stratton-Lake. New York: Oxford University Press, 2002.

Szawarski, Piotr, and John Oram. "Classic Cases Revisited: Baby Theresa and the Definition of Death." *Journal of the Intensive Care Society* 16 (2015): 222–225.

Summary

The ethical history and moral standards of a profession create a deeper understanding of its nature. Both providers and the public can better understand the commitments of a profession by understanding the growth of its ethical culture of practice, specifically the values that support action.

Remember Franklin's conundrum. He is confronted by a demanding coach and a frustrated student-athlete whose football career is at risk. Franklin wants to help Phil become healthy so he is able to return to sport, but Phil's health remains questionable. Phil may need more time to build his strength and endurance and may not be ready for the playoffs.

As a member of a profession, Franklin must abide by its moral duties. He must fulfill his value commitments and protect the interests of those who are being served. The healthcare system is based on the special relationship that forms between providers and patients. Franklin's obligations in this relationship demand care, accountability, and trust. As a physical therapist, he is responsible for his choices, and he must recall his commitments. To protect the integrity of his profession, Franklin cannot be swayed by the coach's interests. In order to protect trust, Franklin must engage in honest, clear communication that puts his patient first. Franklin decides to meet with Phil in order to understand the complexity of his patient's suffering. Franklin explains his concerns about Phil returning to sport too quickly. He commits to honoring his patient's autonomy and to helping him manage this difficult and stressful time.

Physical therapy is an important care-based and service-oriented profession. Professionals must learn the knowledge, skills, and techniques to be competent practitioners. They must also see themselves as role models, advocate for their profession, understand their professional and moral commitments, and maintain community relationships based on trust. Physical therapists have an overriding and fundamental fiduciary obligation to always act in the best interests of their patients.

Comprehension Questions

Johnson, *Three Classical Moral Theories: Critical Frameworks for Deliberation*

1. What makes Utilitarianism a consequentialist moral theory?

2. Why does Mill think that morality should be understood as a social enterprise?

3. According to Kant, what does the first formulation of the Categorical Imperative require of us?

4. What important ethical guidance does Kant's second formulation of the Categorical Imperative provide?

5. What distinguishes Utilitarianism and Deontology from Virtue Ethics?

6. How does Aristotle describe virtue?

7. If virtues and vices are both character traits, what makes them different?

Noddings, *Why Care About Caring?*

1. How does Noddings answer the question, "Why care about caring?"

2. What makes an Ethics of Care different than principle-driven, "mathematical" strategies?

3. How does Noddings define "care"?

4. What kind of relationship best illustrates the moral meaning of "care"?

Johnson, *The Moral Pillars of Biomedical Ethics*

1. What are the four principles of biomedical ethics and why are they important?

2. What obligation does a duty of beneficence impose on clinicians?

3. Why is nonmaleficence a fundamental pillar of the healthcare industry?

4. What does respect for autonomy require of providers?

5. What makes justice an important principle of action for healthcare workers?

Ada's Story

Developing Your Moral Imagination: Critical Thinking Questions

1. What values are at stake in Ada's situation?

2. If you were Ada, how would you rank the applicable values? What value would motivate you to act?

3. What moral theories resonate with you? Why?

4. Why are the principles of biomedical ethics important for healthcare providers and institutions?

A History of Ethics in Physical Therapy

Franklin's Story

Over the past five weeks, Franklin, a physical therapist, has been treating Phil, a Division I college football player suffering from a concussion. Phil's coach has recently been checking in on the athlete's rehabilitation. The playoffs are only a few weeks away, and the coach wants his star player back in the game. While Phil is making progress, Franklin is unconvinced that he is ready to return to sport. Franklin worries that returning Phil to the game now may lead to longer term symptoms, such as chronic dizziness and muscle weakness. Another setback could jeopardize Phil's entire football career. Franklin is apprehensive about choosing the course of action that best promotes his patient's interests.

Schema Activation/Response Question

What course of action aligns with Franklin's professional duties and obligations?

Cultivating Professional Values

The APTA core values aim to promote good reasoning. The key values at stake in Franklin's story include:

- **Accountability:** taking responsibility for one's actions and choices
- **Altruism:** sacrificing for others and putting others' needs before your own
- **Collaboration:** working together in pursuit of a shared goal
- **Compassion/Caring:** having kindness and finding importance in the suffering of others

- **Duty:** fulfilling one's commitment to the profession and meeting the public's trust
- **Excellence:** possessing knowledge and skill and acquiring habits of lifelong learning
- **Integrity:** acting in accord with one's personal and professional moral identity
- **Social Responsibility:** doing good for others and helping the larger community

Introduction to the Topic

This unit explores the development of ethics in the physical therapy profession and the advancement of its moral commitments. The reading describes the growth of an ethical culture in physical therapy and elucidates how moral standards are essential for the self-regulation of a profession.

A profession is distinguished by its specialized knowledge, training, self-regulation, and commitment to serve others. A profession's sovereignty is marked not only by its expertise, skill, and technique but also by its articulation of ethical standards. Indeed, an ethical charter forms the basis of a profession. In healthcare, the charter expresses a dedication to caring for the sick, an endorsement of community trust, and a promise to be accountable for one's actions.

The physical therapy profession diverges from other healthcare professions because of its specialized focus on movement and rehabilitation medicine. In the United States, the profession evolved primarily as the result of two dramatic historical events. First, the poliomyelitis epidemic in the 1890s and 1900s caused severe and often permanent physical disabilities among children.[1] Second, World War I resulted in thousands of wounded soldiers in need of rehabilitation.[2] Physical therapy was now recognized as a valuable service to those in need.

When a licensed healthcare provider enters into professional practice, they are bound by the standards of professional and ethical conduct. For physical therapists, the American Physical Therapy Association's *Code of Ethics for the Physical Therapist and APTA Guide for Professional Conduct* formulates both the standards of conduct and the value commitments of the profession.[3] These shared documents pledge to maintain the public's trust. They supply a moral vocabulary, establish the foundations of ethical care, and express a commitment to be moral. The documents guide moral deliberation and help clinicians to make judgments that align with their commitments to care for the community.

---

[1] Marilyn Moffat, "The History of Physical Therapy Practice in the United States," *Journal of Physical Therapy Education* 17, no. 3 (2003): 15, 17.

[2] Moffat, "The History of Physical Therapy Practice in the United States," 15, 16.

[3] American Physical Therapy Association, *Code of Ethics for the Physical Therapist*, updated August 12, 2020, https://www.apta.org/siteassets/pdfs/policies/codeofethicshods06-20-28-25.pdf; American Physical Therapy Association, *APTA Guide for Professional Conduct*, last modified March 2019, https://www.apta.org/contentassets/7b03fbe1fa5440668a480d2921c5a0b6/apta-guide-for-conduct-pt.pdf.

Introduction to the Reading

The reading by physical therapy professor Nancy R. Kirsch, "A Historical Review of the Development of the Code of Ethics for Physical Therapists," relates the history and development of ethical standards in the physical therapy profession. Kirsch describes how the hallmark of a profession is a code of ethics, which she characterizes as "a dynamic document, based on universal principles and values" that must "provide guidance that is meaningful and applies to the realities of physical therapy practice." Kirsch's essay describes both the development of the physical therapy as a distinctive profession and its ethical formation.

Kirsch begins her analysis with a discussion of the first code of ethics for physiotherapists. Drafted in 1935, this code reveals the standards of physical therapy practice in its infancy. The code was later revised in 1948, 1978, 2011, and 2020. Kirsch notes how most of the revisions to the original code reflect the growth of the profession in connection to social change and progress. The substantial revision culminating in the 2011 edition of the APTA Code of Ethics further reveals a dramatic shift in physical therapy practice. This code acknowledges additional roles of the physical therapist that were previously not addressed, responsibilities as an educator, critical inquirer, consultant, and administrator. The 2011 version also incorporates updated principles of practice that guide how to manage the profession's newly acquired autonomy.

Kirsch concludes her historical narrative with a summary of the 2020 revisions to the APTA Code of Ethics, noting the addition of the core value of collaboration. As physical therapy practice continues to evolve, so does its code of ethics. She surmises that the profession will inevitably tackle ongoing and emerging social changes and problems, such as "social inequity, respect for our environment, and social media challenges." Indeed, Kirsch imagines an expanded future for the profession.

References

American Physical Therapy Association. *Code of Ethics for the Physical Therapist*. Updated August 12, 2020. https://www.apta.org/siteassets/pdfs/policies/codeofethicshods06-20-28-25.pdf.

American Physical Therapy Association. *APTA Guide for Professional Conduct*. Last modified March 2019. https://www.apta.org/contentassets/7b03fbe1fa5440668a480d2921c5a0b6/apta-guide-for-conduct-pt.pdf.

Moffet, Marilyn. "A History of Physical Therapy in the United States." *Journal of Physical Therapy Education* 17, no. 3 (2003): 15–25.

A Historical Review of the Development of the Code of Ethics for Physical Therapists

By Nancy R. Kirsch, PT, DPT, PhD

In 1921 several visionary women met in New York City to recognize the importance of establishing the nascent profession of physical therapy. This group of leaders established the 238-member organization, "American Women's Physical Therapeutic Association." A year later, in an effort to be inclusive and welcome male colleagues, the organization changed the name to the American Physiotherapy Association.

The Association began work on cultivating a professional culture in physical therapy practice. The Australian Council of Professions defines a profession as a "disciplined group of individuals who adhere to ethical standards and who hold themselves out as, and are accepted by the public as possessing special knowledge and skills in a widely recognized body of learning derived from research, education and training at a high level, and who are prepared to apply this knowledge and exercise these skills in the interest of others."[1] Physical therapy was a budding profession.

A profession must have a Code of Ethics as its foundation. A code reflects the activities of the profession and the behaviors expected of the members of that profession. A code of ethics also demands a higher standard of behavior with respect to both the services for the public and their responsibilities to professional colleagues.[2] Consistent with the social contract between a profession and the public, professionals are expected to behave in accordance with ethical standards and the virtues of integrity, trust, and expertise.

A Code of Ethics is a mark of a profession, and professionals are bound by its expectations. Professionals consent to the rights and obligations articulated by the code, and they embrace the

---

[1] Australian Council of Professions, "What is a Profession?" 2003. https://www.professions.org.au

[2] Julia Evetts, "Sociological Analysis of Professionalism: Past, Present and Future," *Comparative Sociology* 10, no. 1 (2011): 1–37.

demands of self-regulation. Collectively, a Code of Ethics upholds and reflects a profession's image, commitments, and reputation.

1935: The First Code of Ethics

In 1935 the first Code of Ethics and Discipline was adopted at the Association's annual meeting in Atlantic City, New Jersey. The original Code clearly defined the responsibilities of the physical therapist and drew a clear picture of the behaviors expected of them. The Code provided direction at that time that evolved over the years as the profession grew and developed. The 1935 version offered the following specific guidance for practicing clinicians:

1. Physicians' prescriptions have primacy in carrying out physical therapy treatments.
2. Physical therapists are prohibited from procuring patients through advertising.
3. Physical therapists cannot criticize physicians and colleagues in the presence of patients.

The 1935 code reflected the early practice patterns of the profession. For example, at the time, physical therapy services were provided by referral only. Physical therapists were professionals, but they lacked autonomy and practiced under the direction of a physician.

1948: Revisions to the Code

The Code of Ethics was revised in 1948, fifteen years after the inaugural code was written. At this stage in the profession's development, physical therapy had proven itself as a valuable service to the community. Indeed, the need for physical therapy services was largely driven by social events. For example, physical therapists found themselves at the epicenter of care during World War I, World War II, and the polio epidemic.

The 1948 revision reflected little growth in professional autonomy for physical therapists, but the development of professional practice standards continued to evolve. For example, key components of the Code incorporated additional guidance for practitioners:

1. The physical therapist must have adequate medical supervision.
2. Diagnosis of disability and prescription of physical therapy is the responsibility of the physician.
3. The physical therapist is expected to give full support to the organization that the physical therapist serves.
4. The physical therapist is guided by the welfare of the patient.
5. The physical therapist has the duty to disclose unethical activities of its members and to testify during an investigation.

Physical therapy practice remained under physicians' supervision, and physical therapists were not encouraged to think independently. The code attempted to acknowledge the relationship between therapists and physicians in order to meet the challenge posed by the ambiguous organizational structure apparent in the therapist-physician dynamic. For example, the code addressed a physical therapist's professional responsibility to be guided by the welfare of the patient. This change reinforced the importance of the relationship between therapists and patients. In addition, a physical therapist's professional responsibility to protect patients was highlighted. This duty further solidified physical therapy's professional status. In addition, the Code also mentions self-regulation, making clear a physical therapist's obligation to self-monitor and to disclose unethical actions.

1978 Revisions to the Code and the *Guide for Professional Conduct*

The Code of Ethics remained essentially unchanged for the next thirty years until it was revised again in 1978.[3] The *Guide to Professional Conduct* was another document drafted and added to the professional guidance documents to assist physical therapists in interpreting the Code of Ethics.

The 1978 revisions generated several significant changes and improved ethical standards to the Code. First, physical therapists must use sound judgment. Second, physical therapists must conduct themselves in a way so as not to discredit the association and the profession. Third, physical therapists must demonstrate loyalty and support for the American Physical Therapy Association (APTA). Fourth, physical therapists must abide by reasonable and sound standards of remuneration. Fifth, physical therapists can practice through written referral only regardless of state law.

During this revisionary phase, an interesting juxtaposition becomes apparent. The code specifies that physical therapists are encouraged to take professional responsibility for their actions, both by exhibiting sound judgment and by conducting themselves as professionals. However, at the time, physical therapists lacked direct access. They could only provide services by referral of a physician. While one jurisdiction permitted direct access to physical therapy services, the Association took a position that regardless of what is legislated for patient access, physical therapists working via direct access would be practicing unethically. Indeed, the practice of direct access was very much on the agenda for physical therapy as a service-oriented healthcare discipline.

---

[3] During this period, the Standards of Ethical Conduct for the Physical Therapy Assistant was drafted as a guide for professional and ethical behavior.

2011 Developments to the Code

Over the next thirty years the Code of Ethics continued to evolve consistent with changes in physical therapy practice and the healthcare system. By 2009, the Code of Ethics had advanced to incorporate 11 principles of conduct.[4] The following standards were included in the code:[5]

1. Respect the rights and dignity/provide competent care

2. Trustworthy

3. Comply with laws and regulations

4. Professional competence for the PT and competence for the PTA

5. Protect the public from unethical, illegal, incompetent acts

6. High standards: Practice/Research/Education

7. Address health needs of society

8. Respect colleagues and other health care professionals

9. Sound professional judgment

10. Reasonable remuneration

11. Provide accurate and relevant information to the public

In addition to the rules of conduct, the APTA defined seven core values for the physical therapist. These include accountability, altruism, compassion/caring, excellence, integrity, professional duty, and social responsibility. These values were not directly incorporated into the Code of Ethics. However, they closely aligned with the expected behaviors of the physical therapist.

In the first decade of the 21st century, physical therapists were practicing with a critically important yet outdated core document. The Ethics and Judicial Committee (EJC) of the APTA was charged annually to review both the Code of Ethics and the Guide for Professional Conduct and make recommendations about these documents to the House of Delegates, a self-regulating body. Part of the House's work involves adjudicating ethical issues that come before the committee. Members of the House came to an agreement that the Code of Ethics was not robust enough to provide needed guidance to help physical therapists respond to the many contemporary ethical issues impacting professional behavior.

In 2005, the EJC began a process to comprehensively evaluate the Code of Ethics, its relevance to practice, and its applicability to contemporary issues. As the EJC embarked on this painstaking review, they also studied similar best practices of other healthcare organizations. The primary question at the

---

[4] By 2009, the Standards of Ethical Conduct for the PTA had seven principles.

[5] The first five rules were shared by both physical therapists and physical therapy assistants. The remaining rules applied to the physical therapist only. Physical therapy assistants were also expected to follow standards of guidance relating to: (1) supervision and direction of the physical therapist and (2) judgment commensurate with education and legal qualifications.

core of the investigation as the profession embraced vision 2020 and the future of PT practice was, "Do the APTA core documents guide the autonomous practice of physical therapy as a doctoring profession?"

The EJC determined that the current document was inadequate to embrace the profession's vision for 2020. It also failed to address the four crucial issues. First, the role of the physical therapist as an educator, critical inquirer, consultant and administrator were not addressed. The Code offered a narrow interpretation of the responsibilities of the physical therapist as a patient client manager only. Second, the Code did not provide direction to help physical therapists manage the responsibilities and demands of autonomous and independent practice. The Code merely acknowledged independent practice yet with incomplete guidance. Third, the Code did not tackle the complexities within the contemporary health care environment. It was general and offered incomplete recommendations for context-specific situations. Fourth, the Code did not focus on the nuances within the relationship between physical therapists and physical therapy assistants. It also did not include recommendations related to interprofessional relationships within the healthcare team.

Perhaps the most disturbing feature of the code was its failure to articulate in any meaningful way a moral understanding unique to the physical therapy profession. Of particular importance, the code did not acknowledge the significance of the patient-therapist relationship. This relationship requires that the therapist appreciates the privilege of working with patients and the obligations associated with the patient therapeutic interaction. In light of the glaring deletions, the APTA Board of Directors, the APTA's governing body, agreed to an extensive review of the Code of Ethics and appointed a task force to undertake this significant undertaking.[6]

Improving documents that aim to guide moral behavior requires extensive resources and input from multiple sources. Since a code reveals the moral fiber of a profession, a process such as this must be systematic. A task force consisting of 13 physical therapists (including 4 current EJC members), 1 physical therapist assistant, 1 student and 1 physical therapy regulator was appointed by the Board to formulate and initiate the process.[7] The entire process took almost four years from inception to completion. The new code reflected the current practice environment, projected where practice was anticipated to progress in the future, and was consistent with the APTA vision statement that envisioned a doctoring profession with patients having direct access to physical therapy services.

A Code of Ethics must be a dynamic document. It must clearly articulate universal principles and values that codify a profession's duties and moral expectations. A code must provide guidance that is both meaningful and applicable to the realities of professional practice. The Code must also be assimilated into professional practice and be recognized as the core foundational document for

---

[6] The APTA Board of Directors also agreed to reexamine the Standards for Ethical Conduct for the Physical Therapy Assistant to see if better alignment could be achieved between the two documents. The need to reflect the collaborative and integrative relationship among physical therapists and physical therapy assistants was apparent.

[7] To ensure that the documents complimented each other, the process of revising the Code of Ethics was completed in unison with the Standards of Ethical Conduct for the Physical Therapy Assistant.

ethical behavior. Ethical decision-making is challenging. It is a learned skill that takes practice. Understanding the nature of a profession's ethical expectations and learning how to apply the Code promotes effective decision-making. To cultivate an ethical culture, professionals need meaningful opportunities to apply the principles and concepts that are representative of their profession.

Table 2.1.1 Comprehensive Revision Timeline Culminating in the 2011 Code of Ethics

Date	Action
June 2006	EJC recommendation to establish a task force to review and revise the APTA core ethics documents approved by the APTA Board of Directors
January–June 2007	Survey to the membership, data collection and review regarding ethical issues confronting physical therapists in contemporary practice.
September 2007	Task force drafts documents for review by the APTA Board of Directors
March 2008	APTA Board of Directors approves draft for comment
September 1–October 30, 2008	Survey of members comments, review by committee members
January 2009	Co-chairs complete the integration of the survey feedback into the draft documents and submit final edit to the Board of Directors
March, 2009	APTA Board of Directors approves the Draft of the revised Code of Ethics and Standards of Ethical Conduct
March 2009	APTA Board of Directors submits final documents for the 2009 House of Delegates
June 2009	APTA House of Delegates reviews and approves the new Code of Ethics and Standards of Ethical Conduct
September 2009–June 2010	Dissemination of documents and education about the new Code of Ethics for the membership and stakeholders
July 1, 2010	New Code of Ethics and Standards of Ethical Conduct go into effect

The APTA's comprehensive review produced the 2011 Code of Ethics that was fundamentally different from the previous versions. The design of the Code provided inclusive guidance for physical therapists, acknowledging their various professional roles. A preamble was drafted and added to the new Code. It identifies the contemporary roles of the physical therapist, specifically noting the "special obligation of the physical therapist to empower, educate, and enable those with impairments, activity limitations, participation restrictions, and disabilities to facilitate greater independence, health, wellness and enhanced quality of life." The amended format of the code was designed to be inclusive, using lettered principles that expand upon the numbered principles, clarifying intent, meaning, and application. All principles begin with the common phrase of "physical therapists shall" raising every principle to the level of an ethical obligation. The core values of the physical therapy profession are also incorporated into the code and associated with each group of principles. The preamble further delineates the ethical obligation of all physical therapists as defined by the American Physical Therapy Association. The preamble concisely asserts the purpose of the Code of Ethics and specifies those who are bound by its standards. The purposes of the Code are the following:

1. Provide standards of behavior and performance that form the basis of professional accountability to the public.

2. Provide guidance for physical therapists facing ethical challenges.

3. Educate physical therapists, students, other health care professionals, regulators and the public regarding the ethical obligations of the physical therapist.

4. Establish the standards by which the American Physical Therapy Association can determine if a physical therapist has engaged in unethical conduct.

The new Code clarified and refined long standing ethical obligations that were part of the original code. Ethical obligations toward patients and colleagues were codified. Duties to respect the virtues of truthfulness, honesty, and integrity were incorporated. The revised documents, recognizing the complexities of contemporary practice go beyond the original code, and provide guidance to individual, institutional, and societal realms.

The 2011 revision process also incorporated new guidance reflecting what the profession identified as current and social issues of ethical concern impacting physical therapy practice. Professional competence and the importance of lifelong engagement was codified as the professional's responsibility. Standards for effective service-delivery and good business practice were incorporated; principles encouraged professionals to cultivate effective habits that work in patients' best interests. Finally, the Code acknowledges the critical need to address the social determinants of health, and how they impact society, patients, and the profession. The Code stresses the crucial need for making physical therapy services accessible. Indeed, these principles are very important additions, but they will not be the last.

Table 2.1.2 Revised Code of Ethics

Principle/Standard	Ethical Guidance	Added in 2010
1	Duty to all individuals	
2	Duty to patients/clients	
3	Accountability for sound judgment	
4	Integrity in relationships	
5	Fulfilling legal and professional obligations	
6	Lifelong acquisition of knowledge, skills, abilities	X
7	Organizational behavior and business practices	X
8	Meeting the health needs of society	X

Conclusion: 2020 Updates to the Code

As recently as 2020, changes have been made to the Code providing additional clarifying language. For example, the Code incorporates the new core virtue of collaboration. Acknowledging the inter-professional dynamic within physical therapy practice, this value articulates clinicians' obligations to work with others both within and outside of their discipline in order to provide the best care possible. As society changes, future revisions may be necessitated. All professions must mature and adapt to the complexities that arise with social change. Current issues in our world, such as social inequity, respect for our environment, and social media challenges, will need to be addressed. Indeed, the impact of social conflict and unethical behavior affects not only patient care but also the commitments of the healthcare profession. How issues like these are tackled will define how the profession of physical therapy grows in the future.

References

APTA Code of Ethics. https://www.apta.org/apta-and-you/leadership-and-governance/policies/code-of-ethics-for-the-physical-therapist

APTA Standards of Ethical Conduct: https://www.apta.org/apta-and-you/leadership-and-governance/policies/standards-of-ethical-conduct-for-the-physical-therapist-assistant

Australian Council of Professions: https://www.professions.org.au

Evetts, Julia. "Sociological Analysis of Professionalism: Past, Present and Future." *Comparative Sociology* 10, no. 1 (2011): 1-37.

··

Summary

Healthcare providers face competing demands. Some demands are personal, some are professional, and some are ethical. Moreover, conflicts can arise between these demands. Understanding the complexities of the various obligations at stake can be difficult. Sometimes clinicians disagree about the right course of action and are unable to find common ground on which they can work together.

Learning ethics can help clinicians cultivate constructive habits to respond to problematic moral conflicts. However, understanding ethics involves more than memorizing principles of right and wrong. Understanding requires the ability to apply ethical tools to help you navigate through the tough situations that have no easy answers.

Recall Ada's situation. She wants to help Michael, but he is not the only stakeholder in this case. Ada has obligations to her employer, her patients, and her family. If Ada provides care to Michael at no cost, she may upset her employer, the facility may suffer, and other patients may be harmed. Clearly, many interests compete with one another. Ada wants to do the right thing, but she is uncertain about what the right thing to do is. She wants to help as many people as she can and minimize any negative consequences.

Given Ada's role as a healthcare provider, we must ask what are her responsibilities? The principles of biomedical ethics clearly codify the moral expectations involved. She must promote the good, avoid or minimize the risk of harm, respect people, and ensure that justice is fulfilled. In addition, the values of her profession, codified in the APTA Code of Ethics, also apply.

The complexity of Ada's situation illuminates why ethics is challenging. Sometimes more than one action is possible, and fulfilling duties can involve compromise. Identifying the clinical and practical details is important, but also consider whose interests are at stake. Consider your duties as a provider. Consider the benefits and burdens. Consider your values.

As Ada reflects upon the situation, she thinks back to why she became a physical therapist. She wants to help people to live well. Her work requires a meaningful commitment to serve people—indeed, all people—regardless of their ability to pay. However, Ada knows she has additional commitments to her employer and the facility. Ada cannot provide all the care that Michael needs, because her clinic and her patients will likely suffer. Ada further realizes that if she assumes his care on top of her case load, she will have less time with her family. Ada decides to consult with other colleagues who are willing to collaborate in Michael's care.

A foundational knowledge of basic theoretical ideals is essential to navigating difficult ethical terrain. Most people have a clear sense of right and wrong but studying ethics will help you to refine the skills you need to find practical solutions to complex situations when the right answer is not clear. Ethics provides a valuable lens for focusing on complexities. Studying ethics can help you understand what you value so that you can cultivate dispositions to fulfill the good. Developing habits that promote awareness and reflection are essential to becoming a person of integrity, someone who has a strong moral foundation, a sense of humility, and accountability for commitments.

As a healthcare provider, you represent your profession and must promote the public trust. In so doing, you have a duty to fulfill the professional responsibilities, obligations that often ask more than the bare minimum. Moral training and reflection provide practical value; these skills help you to develop consistent thinking habits so at the end of the day you can sleep well. Ethical reflection helps to challenge assumptions and stimulate the moral imagination. Ethics encourages us to look at the world in a different way. Through ethics, we understand that rights come with obligations to both others and ourselves. We do not live in isolation from other people; we live together in community. We ought to learn and practice how to live well and, in so doing, how to do good for others.

Comprehension Questions

Kirsch, *A Historical Review of the Development of the Code of Ethics for Physical Therapists.*

1. What are some principles in the 1935 American Physiotherapist Association's Code of Ethics?
2. How does Kirsch describe the features of a profession?
3. What are some of the significant changes to the APTA Code of Ethics made in 2011? Why are these changes important to the physical therapy profession?
4. What is the most recent 2020 addition to the Code of Ethics?

Franklin's Story

Developing Your Moral Imagination: Critical Thinking Questions

1. If you were in Franklin's situation, what would you do?
2. What goals and APTA core values should factor into and guide Franklin's decision?
3. In weighing options, how should Franklin balance Phil's current and future interests?
4. What is the significance of ethical standards for a profession?

UNIT III

Choosing to Be Ethical

....

Gail's Story

Initially, Gail was thrilled to start her first job in an outpatient orthopedic clinic specializing in sports medicine and the rehabilitation of musculoskeletal conditions. After three months in the post, however, she finds herself struggling with demanding productivity requirements and other administrative burdens, including the electronic medical record (EMR). On average, Gail works ten-hour days in the clinic and is expected to see three to four patients per hour. After she is finished with patient care, she then must spend hours updating the EMR. Gail spoke with the manager of the clinic about the steep productivity demands. She explained that much of the documentation is redundant and burdensome, and that it is affecting her ability to treat the unique needs of each patient. He responded that the productivity requirements were company policy and suggested that she should reevaluate the time she spends with each patient. He said that if she could not keep up with standard expectations, he would terminate her employment at the clinic. Gail believes the clinic's policy is onerous and not patient-centric. However, as a recent graduate and inexperienced clinician, she feels powerless to change anything.

Schema Activation/Response Question

How should Gail respond to the conflict?

Cultivating Professional Values

The APTA core values aim to promote good reasoning. The key values at stake in Gail's story include:

- **Accountability:** taking responsibility for one's actions and choices
- **Collaboration:** working together in pursuit of a shared goal
- **Duty:** fulfilling one's commitments to the profession
- **Integrity:** acting in accord with one's personal and professional moral identity

Introduction to the Topic

Choosing to be ethical is not easy. The stressors that arise in healthcare affect our ability to make good choices. This unit begins with moral distress and burnout, two factors influencing moral behavior. While clinical distress and clinician burnout are not new phenomena, they raise important questions about the healthcare system and illuminate the challenges that providers face. Further, the readings highlight the moral dimensions of communication and the importance of character dispositions like courage and integrity. These topics offer an ethical perspective on the challenges and vulnerabilities unique to healthcare providers and shed light on the significance of professional values—notably, accountability, duty, and integrity.

Introduction to the Readings

Moral Distress, Burnout, and Moral Injury

The healthcare environment is undoubtedly fulfilling, but also challenging and stressful. Interacting with patients when they are vulnerable can take a toll on clinicians. The nature of healthcare practice, coupled with institutional burdens and administrative pressures, can conflict with the fundamental reason why clinicians chose their career in the first place: to help people.

Feeling distress in a fast-paced environment is common. Distress generally involves the experience of suffering or anxiety when we struggle to maintain the pace in the face of pressures that feel out of our control. However, what makes distress moral?

Moral distress accounts for the psychological, physiological, behavioral, and emotional suffering that transpires when a person feels morally compromised. In 1984, Andrew Jameton presented a description of moral distress that highlights how constraints can impair people's ability to act on the basis of their moral values and professional obligations.[1] According to Jameton, the experience of moral distress "arises when one knows the right thing to do, but institutional constraints make it nearly impossible to pursue the right course of action."[2] Moral distress happens when a person is prevented from doing the right thing or when doing the right thing can place a person in personal or professional jeopardy. Often, healthcare providers know the right thing to do, but institutional restrictions inhibit them from doing what they believe is right. In moral distress, one's moral sense of self, those ethical values that constitute character, are threatened.

---

[1] Andrew Jameton, *Nursing Practice: The Ethical Issues* (Englewood, NJ: Prentice-Hall, 1984).

[2] Jameton, *Nursing Practice,* 6.

In the first reading selection "A Broader Understanding of Moral Distress," Stephen M. Campbell, Connie M. Ulrich, and Christine Grady evaluate traditional characterizations of moral distress and illuminate its pervasive nature, its various causes, and its impact on provider's well-being. They propose a comprehensive taxonomy of numerous factors that can provoke its occurrence such as uncertainty, bad luck, and guilt by association. These influences, they note, can also overlap. Dynamics that trigger moral distress compromise individuals' abilities to make moral choices that align with their moral beliefs. For example, circumstances when a person is unsure of the right action or when the right act results in a bad outcome can cause a person to feel morally compromised provoking feelings of distress.

In healthcare, clinicians often encounter situations where they lack the knowledge to make a moral decision. When ignorance and uncertainty interfere and providers feel they cannot identify the right course of action, they often experience moral distress. Moral distress can influence a clinician's decisions, which in turn can lead to less-than-optimal outcomes or, even worse, patient harm.

One dangerous effect of moral distress is burnout. In the 1970s, Herbert Freudenberger described burnout as a syndrome involving physical, behavioral, and psychological symptoms, including anger, powerlessness, cynicism, and frustration.[3] According to Freudenberger, burnout arises when an employee is overcommitted to an overly demanding job.

Freudenberger's research focused on the role of individuals' behaviors in becoming burned out. Various proposed causes included inadequate personal self-care or the failure to set boundaries. In this incomplete model, the individual bears sole responsibility for becoming burned out as well as the responsibility for resolving the condition.

While only a handful of studies on burnout in physical therapy practice exist, anecdotal stories indicate burnout is indeed a problem in the profession.[4] Factors including high productivity demands, the electronic medical record, fluctuating reimbursement rates, and the burden of student loan debt all act as stressors that provoke moral distress and lead to burnout.[5] Physical therapists confront multiple obligations that often wind up in conflict. For instance, while clinicians swore an oath to care for patients, they must also answer to other stakeholders, such as employers and insurers. Burnout, moreover, is insidious. As moral distress builds and a person becomes burned out, moral injury results.

---

[3] Herbert J. Freudenberger, "The Staff Burn-Out Syndrome in Alternative Institutions," *Psychotherapy: Theory, Research, and Practice* 12, no.1 (1975): 73–82.

[4] Troy Elliot, "Understanding and Avoiding Burnout," *PT in Motion*, November 2020, https://www.apta.org/apta-magazine/2020/11/01/understanding-and-avoiding-burnout; Eric Ries, "Beating Burnout," *PT in Motion*, February 2019, https://www.apta.org/apta-magazine/2019/02/01/beating-burnout; Justin Berry, "Occupational Burnout in Physical Therapy: Clinical Implications and Strategies for Reduction" (presentation at the 2017 Annual FSBPT Meeting, East Grand Forks, MN), https://www.fsbpt.org/Portals/0/documents/free-resources/Spring2018ForumOccupationalBurnoutinPhysicalTherapy.pdf; Meredith V. Castin, "Physical Therapy Burnout in Destroying our Profession," *CoreMedical Group* (blog), October 18, 2017, https://blog.coremedicalgroup.com/physical-therapy-burnout; Brenda J. Wandling and Barbara S. Smith, "Burnout in Orthopaedic Physical Therapists," *Journal of Orthopaedic and Sports Physical Therapy* 26, no. 3 (1997): 124–130.

[5] Ries, "Beating Burnout"; Castin, "Physical Therapy Burnout."

Psychologist Jonathan Shay coined the concept of moral injury.[6] Shay counselled Vietnam War veterans and observed the symptoms of the psychological injuries they endured from the trauma of war. In some cases, he initially thought his patients were suffering from posttraumatic stress disorder. However, he noticed an important difference in many of the veterans' narratives. Some of his patients were suffering deeply from an injury that challenged their moral sense of self. This led him to the new term "moral injury."

Posttraumatic stress disorder is a form of psychological injury caused by an event that threatens physical harm, injury, or even life. Posttraumatic stress disorder is an existential threat; it is harm done to a person's sense of security. Moral injury, in contrast, is a form of psychological injury that arises when a person participated in, failed to prevent, or bore witness to what they believed to be morally wrong.[7] Moral injury is the harm done to people when their moral beliefs are betrayed. Shay claims moral injury has three components: First, moral injury involves "a betrayal of what's right." Second, the betrayal occurs "by someone who holds a legitimate authority (e.g., in the military—a leader)." Third, the betrayal and the injury happen "in a high stakes situation."[8]

Shay further describes the effects of moral injury on character. He says moral injury "deteriorates their character; their ideals, ambitions, and attachments begin to change and shrink ... and destroy the capacity for trust."[9] Moral injury can shatter integrity, and integrity is what helps to maintain unity within a person. The choices a person feels forced to make have a cumulative effect that over time can change their character. Moral injury suggests how institutional structures cause harm by placing a person in a situation with an impossible choice: to sacrifice one obligation in order to fulfill another.

Burnout is something *within* in a person, whereas moral injury is something that happens *to* a person.[10] Moral injury "describes the challenges of simultaneously knowing what care patients need but being unable to provide it due to constraints that are beyond our control. Moral injury is the presence of the ever-present double bind in healthcare: Do we take care of our patients, the hospital, the insurer, the EMR, the health care system, or our productivity metrics first? "[11] Reframing the nature of burnout and moral distress and acknowledging its external influences illuminates the need to restructure the healthcare environment in order to correct the occurrence of morally impossible situations. Professional institutions must work to prevent established structures from morally compromising clinicians.

---

[6] Jonathan Shay, "Moral Injury," *Psychoanalytic Psychology* 31, no. 2 (2014): 182–191.

[7] Simon G. Talbot and Wendy Dean, "Physicians Aren't 'Burning Out.' They're Suffering From Moral Injury," *STAT News, July 26, 2018, https://www.statnews.com/2018/07/26/physicians-not-burning-out-they-are-suffering-moral-injury/*; Sonya B. Norman and Shira Maguen, "Moral Injury," U.S. Department of Veterans Affairs, accessed October 5, 2020, https://www.ptsd.va.gov/professional/treat/cooccurring/moral_injury.asp.

[8] Shay, "Moral Injury," 183.

[9] Shay, "Moral Injury," 186.

[10] Wendy Dean, Simon Talbot, and Austin Dean, "Reframing Clinical Distress: Moral Injury Not Burnout," *Federal Practitioner* 36, no. 9 (September 2019): 400–402.

[11] W. Dean, Talbot, and A. Dean, "Reframing," 401.

The Importance of Communication, Moral Integrity, and Courage

Moral integrity is a complex combination of virtues that constitute the whole character of a morally good person. These virtues are valuable. They define who we are, and they help us to live well. To be good people, we must stand up for what is right, for our moral commitments, and for the values of our profession. We cultivate moral integrity and manifest moral identity by remaining true to moral virtues and commitments. Moral integrity unites our sense of self, connects us to our values, offers us a clear path, and keeps us whole.

Most people will inevitably confront ethical conflicts at some point in their lives. Ethics education teaches the practical skills needed to cultivate and maintain integrity. Professionals who recognize what they value will be critical in moments of crisis. Aligning behaviors with moral expectations and the values of the physical therapy profession will strengthen character. Physical therapists promote a climate of trust by modelling and communicating their personal values and the value of their profession.

Practical conflicts will inevitably emerge, and better communication skills can play a role in how clinicians respond to conflicting choices and situations that compromise integrity. In the second reading, "Communicating with Integrity," Rita Manning and Scott Stroud offer recommendations for effective, ethical, and professional communication. The authors highlight two basic ethical standards for communication: "First, in communicating with others you must respect them as persons with moral value. Second, in order to transform your environment into one that is more ethical, you must be able to communicate your values to others in an articulate and persuasive way." From the author's description of effective communication, we can conclude we should strive to prevent conflict, rather than face it once it has developed. Being proactive is an admirable strategy.

Today's healthcare environment is full of obstacles that challenge our moral integrity. In a system burdened by political and financial pressures, these stressors threaten to push us off balance. Often, we see no satisfactory path forward. When communication is not enough to resolve a crisis and your moral integrity is at stake, what do you do?

The courageous person can appropriately respond in the face of danger and adversity. Moral courage is a virtue, and the manifestation of moral integrity in action. According to Aristotle, courage is a mean that lies in between two extremes—namely, the excess of recklessness and the deficiency of cowardice. Aristotle said the courageous "fear what is fearful: but he will endure it in the right way."[12] The courageous person is prudent and thoughtful—they know when to face danger and when to take cover.

The meaning of courage is frequently referenced in connection to a soldier's character on the battlefield. Courage, a desirable response to physical harm and danger, can be explored off the battlefield as well. In the third reading, "Moral Courage," philosopher Matthew Pianalto examines competing accounts of courage. He describes the differences between traditional or physical courage and moral courage. Pianalto illustrates how bravery goes beyond physical force or violence; it involves

---

[12] Aristotle, *Nicomachean Ethics,* trans. Martin Ostwald (New Jersey: Prentice Hall, 1999), 70.

respecting others by engaging them as rational and autonomous beings. He defines moral courage as "acting for a moral cause despite the presence of danger in a way that respects the moral agency of others." The author explains that moral courage is the mark of integrity, and "is something to which we should aspire." Pianalto shows us that true moral courage requires intellectual humility. We should not fight every battle; rather, we must act in a way that makes prudent use of our resources, respects others, builds community, defends justice, and promotes self-confidence.

References

Aristotle. *Nicomachean Ethics.* Translated by Martin Ostwald. Prentice Hall, 1999.

Berry, Justin. "Occupational Burnout in Physical Therapy: Clinical Implications and Strategies for Reduction." Presentation at the 2017 FSBPT Annual Meeting, East Grand Forks, MN. https://www.fsbpt.org/Portals/0/documents/free-resources/Spring2018ForumOccupational BurnoutinPhysicalTherapy.pdf.

Castin, Meredith V. "Physical Therapy Burnout is Destroying Our Profession." *CoreMedical Group* (blog). Accessed October 5, 2020 https://covalentcareers.com/resources/physical-therapy-burnout/

Dean, Wendy, Simon Talbot, and Austin Dean. "Reframing Clinical Distress: Moral Injury Not Burnout." *Federal Practitioner* 36, no. 9 (September 2019): 400–402.

Elliot, Troy. "Understanding and Avoiding Burnout." *APTA Magazine.* November 1, 2020. https://www.apta.org/apta-magazine/2020/11/01/understanding-and-avoiding-burnout.

Freudenberger, Herbert J. "The Staff Burn-out Syndrome in Alternative Institutions." *Psychotherapy: Theory, Research, and Practice* 12, no. 1 (1975): 73–82.

Jameton, Andrew. *Nursing Practice: The Ethical Issues.* Prentice-Hall, 1984.

Norman, Sonya B., and Shira Maguen. "Moral Injury." U.S. Department of Veterans Affairs. Accessed October 5, 2020 https://www.ptsd.va.gov/professional/treat/cooccurring/moral_injury.asp.

Ries, Eric. "Beating Burnout." *PT in Motion*, February 2019. https://www.apta.org/apta-magazine/2019/02/01/beating-burnout.

Shay, Jonathan. "Moral Injury." *Psychoanalytic Psychology* 31, no. 2 (2014): 182–191.

Talbot, Simon G., and Wendy Dean. "Physicians aren't 'burning out.' They're suffering from moral injury." *STAT News,* July 26, 2018. https://www.statnews.com/2018/07/26/physicians-not-burning-out-they-are-suffering-moral-injury/.

Wandling, Brenda J., and Barbara S. Smith. "Burnout in Orthopaedic Physical Therapists." *Journal of Orthopaedic and Sports Physical Therapy* 26, no. 3 (September 1997): 124–130.

Selections from "A Broader Understanding of Moral Distress"

By Stephen M. Campbell, Bentley University
    Connie M. Ulrich, University of Pennsylvania
    Christine Grady, National Institutes of Health

O n the traditional view, moral distress arises only in cases where an individual believes she knows the morally right thing to do but fails to perform that action due to various constraints. We seek to motivate a broader understanding of moral distress. We begin by presenting six types of distress that fall outside the bounds of the traditional definition and explaining why they should be recognized as forms of moral distress. We then propose and defend a new and more expansive definition of moral distress and examine how it can enable the development of a taxonomy of moral distress.

Keywords: decision making, medicine, moral theory, professional ethics, professional-patient relationship

Moral distress has become a well-established issue of concern in the nursing literature and is increasingly getting attention in other domains of healthcare. According to Andrew Jameton, who first introduced the topic in the 1980s, "*Moral distress* arises when one knows the right thing to do, but institutional constraints make it nearly impossible to pursue the right course of action" (1984, 6). Since the time of this initial characterization, the phenomenon of moral distress has been discussed, defined, and researched by several authors. While there are subtle variations in how different authors have understood it, the following are widely held to be defining elements of moral distress:[1]

---

[1] For some representative characterizations of moral distress that include one or more of these features, see Jameton (1984, 6); Wilkinson (1987–1988, 16–24); Jameton (1993); Webster and Baylis (2000, 218); Corley (2002); Hanna (2004, 76); Rushton (2006, 161); American Association of Critical-Care Nurses (2008); Canadian Nurses Association (2008); McCarthy and Deady (2008, 254, 257); Epstein and Hamric (2009); Austin et al. (2009, 58); Chen (2009); Epstein and Hamric (2009); Ulrich, Hamric, and Grady (2010, 20); Epstein and Delgado (2010); and Hamric (2014).

Stephen M. Campbell, Connie M. Ulrich, and Christine Grady, Selections from "A Broader Understanding of Moral Distress," *The American Journal of Bioethics*, vol. 16, no. 12, pp. 2-7, 9. Copyright © 2016 by Taylor & Francis Group. Reprinted with permission.

1. It arises when one believes one knows the morally right thing to do (or avoid doing), but one's ability to do this is constrained by internal and/or external factors.
2. It comes in two phases. There is "initial distress" at the time of potential action (or inaction); later, there is "reactive distress" or "moral residue" that occurs in response to the initial episode of moral distress.
3. It involves the compromising of one's moral integrity or the violation of one's core values.

This is the prevailing understanding of what moral distress is.

Our purpose in this [reading] is to motivate a broader understanding of moral distress. There is a wider range of cases that can sensibly be framed as moral distress, and it is important to recognize them as such. Embracing a broader conception of moral distress does not in any way undermine the relevance or importance of the groundbreaking work that has been done on this topic over the past several years. It simply implies that this previous work has focused on one type of moral distress. In the first section, we present six cases that fall outside bounds of the traditional characterization of moral distress. We argue that it is desirable for a definition of moral distress to encompass them. In the second section, we propose a new definition that accommodates all six cases, as well as the cases accommodated by the traditional definition of moral distress. In the third section, we respond to worries that this new definition is overly broad. In the fourth section, we take some first steps toward the development of a taxonomy of moral distress.

The Case for Broadening Our Understanding of Moral Distress

The purpose of this section is to motivate the need to broaden the traditional characterization of moral distress. Our strategy is to present six cases of distress and explain why they should be understood to be forms of moral distress. It should first be clarified that the inclusion of our six cases cannot be motivated by an appeal to the meaning of "moral distress." Although the words "moral" and "distress" are pieces of natural language, the phrase "moral distress" is a term of art. It was first coined in 1984 for the purpose of naming a phenomenon that was observed in nursing practice, and the phrase has had life almost exclusively within the medical and bioethics literature. For this reason, we are happy to grant that "moral distress" means whatever the scholars writing about it have taken it to mean. Since the prevailing understanding of moral distress in the relevant literature excludes the six cases, a brute appeal to meaning does nothing to motivate their inclusion.

What can serve to motivate the inclusion of the six cases is reflection on the features of moral distress that help to explain why health care professionals and bioethicists have had a sustained interest in this topic. The phenomenon of moral distress is, first and foremost, a practical problem. In the nursing profession, its problematic nature largely consists in its adverse effects on the well-being of nurses, the quality of patient care, and nurse retention (Kelly 1998; Corley et al., 2001; Corley 2002; Hamric and Blackhall 2007; Hamric, Borchers, and Epstein 2012; Whitehead et al., 2015). Of course, it is likely that any type of on-the-job distress or frustration can contribute to such problems—including, for instance, distress that stems from having an overbearing coworker or being continually exposed to the suffering and death of patients. But there is something especially problematic and worrisome about distress that arises when individuals feel morally compromised or tainted in some way. As we see it, this is what distinguishes moral distress from other kinds of distress. This may explain why the topic of moral distress, as opposed to mere distress, has received so much attention. Arguably, bioethicists, policymakers, and health care administrators have special reason to try to eliminate, or at least mitigate, this kind of distress in health care contexts. Admittedly, this talk of being "morally compromised" or "morally tainted" is rather vague. Even so, these expressions are useful starting points for thinking about what moral distress is and why it is often important to address it.

Although none of our six cases involves moral distress as traditionally conceived, each involves an individual in a health care context experiencing distress because he or she feels morally compromised in some way. Each of the cases describes a type of experience that certainly could, and probably often does, contribute to a loss of well-being, a diminishment of job satisfaction, poorer job performance, and burnout. As we hope to show, there appears to be no principled reason why a definition of moral distress should exclude these cases.

Moral Uncertainty

A newly appointed general surgeon who has just finished his residency training is assigned to a disproportionate share of the Medicaid and uninsured cases. These patients are complicated, and many of them suffer with multiple comorbidities due to limited access to primary care and treatment. In fact, several of his patients have already experienced postoperative complications following gastrointestinal surgery, including abdominal sepsis and evisceration. He feels that assigning a new surgeon to these patients is unfair to them since he has less experience than other surgeons. He worries that he might be harming them. He is distressed about this but does not know the best way to respond. One option is to simply continue doing the surgeries to the best of his ability. Alternatively, he could complain to his superiors, though he is worried that he might be labeled as a troublemaker and that some of the surgeries might get delayed. He also considers seeking the advice of a more senior surgeon, but he suspects that he would be told that this is the way the system works and it is good training. He is not sure what the morally best course of action is.

Moral distress is commonly thought to arise only in cases where a person thinks she knows the morally right course of action. No doubt, there are times when we find ourselves in situations in which we think we know exactly what morality demands of us. Still, as illustrated in the case just described, it is all too common that we fall short of having such knowledge. Life as a moral agent is complex, and it is often difficult or impossible to know what the morally right course of action is. One reason for this is that it is no easy matter saying which moral theory or moral principles are correct. Even moral philosophers, whose careers revolve around thinking about ethics, are continually developing, revising, and fine-tuning their own views about morality. Another reason has to do with uncertainty or indeterminacy concerning the professional duties or proper role of different health care professionals and workers. A final reason for moral uncertainty is that we often lack pertinent empirical information about our situation. To appreciate this point, imagine a situation in which a patient is about to consent to a procedure without having adequate information. Jameton (1993, 544) gives the following (nonexhaustive) list of ways in which a nurse might immediately react to this potentially distressing situation:

- Just relate the information to the patient.
- Ask the physician leading questions to elicit the information.
- Step aside with the physician and suggest that he or she reconsider the procedure, or suggest that the physician or nurse give the patient more information.
- Call in the head nurse.
- Resign on the spot.
- Scream.
- Undermine the process.
- Say a prayer.
- Do nothing.

Jameton goes on to list a host of other possible actions the nurse might take soon after the event or that he or she might take if this sort of situation arises regularly (544–45). Given the vast array of possible actions open to us at any given moment, it is no wonder that we often fall short of knowing what the morally right action would be. We often will not know all of the possible actions that are available to us, much less what consequences they would all have—and, as a result, will not know what the right thing to do is. Yet, even in the absence of such knowledge, it is possible for one to experience negative attitudes like guilt or unease. One might have a firm conviction that one did the *wrong* thing without having the faintest clue what the right action would have been. Or one might simply *suspect* that one failed to do the morally right thing, even if one is not at all sure. Distress in the form of guilt or self-criticism can arise under such circumstances.

Mild Distress

An operating-room scrub nurse is frequently assigned to work with a pediatric cardiac surgeon who has a reputation for explosive outbursts in the operating room (OR). The surgeon has screamed profanities at the heart-bypass perfusion team, anesthesiologists, residents, and nurses, and has even been known to throw instruments across the room. The scrub nurse happens to be in the surgeon's good graces and is one of the few people immune to her outbursts. Even so, he finds it troubling to see his colleagues berated and thinks he should intervene in some way. Yet, when these outbursts happen, he feels constrained from saying anything to the surgeon for fear of falling out of favor with her and possibly making the situation worse, which might undermine the cooperation and teamwork needed to save the health or life of the child on the operating-room table. Taken in isolation, each episode is only mildly upsetting to the scrub nurse. Indeed, the first time he experienced the surgeon's behavior, he just rolled his eyes and continued to focus on his work. But these instances of distress have a negative cumulative effect over time.

Discussions of moral distress often give the impression that every episode of moral distress is a dramatic, life-altering affair. The common practice of associating moral distress with the compromise of one's moral integrity, the violation of one's core values, or even the threatening of one's very identity suggests serious moral compromise. And the word "distress" could easily be taken to denote a very strong emotional reaction.

We grant that the most disturbing and significant instances of moral distress will be those that create intense feelings of distress and shake people to their "moral core" by violating their core values or compromising their moral integrity. However, individuals can be morally compromised in less momentous ways that are still damaging and worth addressing (cf. Corley 2002, 637). It can be distressing to be prevented from doing what you think is the morally right thing to do even when the action in question has nothing to do with your core values. People who are morally corrupt can have rare moments of moral conscientiousness and can experience distress if they are kept from acting rightly—even if they do not really have any moral integrity to compromise. Finally, as exemplified in the case just described, there are occasions on which a person finds it only mildly distressing that she is constrained from doing what she thinks is morally best. Episodes of mild distress, when they occur on a regular basis, can have an adverse cumulative effect on those who experience them. The difference between strong and mild distress is a difference only in degree, not in kind. Rather than denying the existence of mild moral distress, we should simply recognize that isolated instances of mild moral distress have lower moral priority than stronger forms.

Delayed Distress

An experienced emergency physician is on duty when a 55-yearold female patient arrives at the emergency department via ambulance after being ejected from the vehicle during a roll over motor vehicle collision. She sustained multiple fractures, severe facial injuries, and a significant closed head injury. The patient was intubated on scene by the paramedics, and cardiopulmonary resuscitation (CPR) is in progress after a traumatic cardiac arrest. Upon arrival, she has no pupillary response and she remains in full cardiac arrest. The emergency physician, nurses, and trauma team immediately continue resuscitation, placing multiple lines, giving meds and blood products in accordance with Advanced Trauma Life Support protocols. Multiple units of blood, IV fluids, and medications are administered in an attempt to get return of spontaneous circulation and manage the patient's injury. After 30 minutes of aggressive resuscitation, the patient has return of spontaneous circulation and is transferred to the OR for a craniotomyto relieve intracranial pressure, which helps stabilize her condition although she is still in critical condition and the team questions the likelihood of a meaningful recovery. On his drive home, the physician begins to reflect on the attempts to resuscitate the woman and is troubled that they were so aggressive for so long. His knowledge and experience told him the chances of a meaningful recovery from her devastating injuries were very low. He wonders about the woman's quality of life and whether aggressive resuscitation was the best option.

On the traditional picture of moral distress, it comes in two stages. First, there is *initial distress*, which is felt at the very time at which one's action is constrained by internal or external factors. This is followed by *reactive distress*, or what some have called "moral residue." It appears to be widely assumed that both initial distress and reactive distress are essential elements of moral distress. Indeed, Jameton, one of the first to explicitly draw the initial/reactive distress distinction, defines reactive distress in terms of initial distress: "Reactive distress is the distress that people feel when they do not act upon their initial distress" (1993, 544). This characterization of reactive distress presupposes the existence of initial distress.[2]

As our case of delayed distress illustrates, it is perfectly possible for a person to fail to have distress at the time of being morally comprised. In emergency situations, the urgent need for action can prevent a person from fully processing the nature of the situation and her actions and, as a result, from feeling the appropriate emotions. Yet, if later reflection leads a person to recognize that she had been constrained from acting in the morally best way and if she feels distress as a result of this, there is no reason why we should not treat this as a case of moral distress. Such a person might be in a mental state nearly identical to that of a morally distressed person who did have initial distress.

We can also imagine scenarios in which one experiences initial distress without reactive distress. After the period of initial distress, any number of events might prevent an individual from experiencing reactive distress. One might forget about the distressing episode (particularly in cases of mild distress), repress the memory of it, formulate a post hoc rationalization of one's behavior, or become occupied with more pressing concerns (such as the death of a loved one). An individual might not have reactive distress because she comes to see her initial distress as inappropriate—perhaps because she gains more information that leads her to revise her moral assessment of the situation. There are also cases where the experience of reactive distress is precluded by a medical condition or death.

In light of these considerations, it is a mistake to insist that initial distress and moral residue are necessary features of moral distress. Cases in which only one or the other occurs still deserve to be treated as cases of moral distress.

Moral Dilemma

A bioethics consultant is called by the pediatric oncology team to get advice about a 13-year-old patient with cancer whose clinical situation is precarious. The team members want to know what they should tell the patient about his diagnosis and prognosis. When the patient was diagnosed over a year ago, his parents were worried that knowledge of his condition would be overwhelming and cause him unnecessary distress. They asked the team not to give him details about his disease. Despite many months of aggressive

---

[2] See also Webster and Baylis (2000, 218).

treatment, his cancer is progressing and he is experiencing some debilitating complications from the treatment. The parents are still adamant that he should not be given details about his condition, and the team does not know how to respond. After meeting with the patient and his parents, the bioethics consultant feels torn between respecting the wishes of the parents who know their son and have his best interests at heart, and showing respect for the patient and his welfare by advising the team to disclose what they know about his situation that might help him make informed decisions. Each option seems morally regrettable: Either they deceive this patient about his condition, or they violate the parents' wishes and give the patient information that is likely to cause him distress. The bioethics consultant thinks there are equally good arguments to be made against each of these choices. He ultimately recommends disclosing information to the patient, but he feels some guilt about making this recommendation.

When Jameton first introduced the phenomenon of moral distress, he contrasted it with two other kinds of cases: cases of moral uncertainty, and moral dilemmas. We have already challenged the idea that moral distress and moral uncertainty are mutually exclusive phenomena. We now wish to suggest that there is also some overlap between moral dilemmas and moral distress. Moral dilemmas "arise when two (or more) clear moral principles apply, but they support mutually inconsistent courses of action" (Jameton 1984, 6). Thus, if moral distress (as traditionally conceived) arises in cases where morality pulls a person in one direction but constraints pull her in another, moral dilemmas are cases in which morality itself pulls a person in competing directions. As a result, dilemmas are cases in which one cannot avoid doing something morally regrettable.

It seems a mistake to define moral distress in such a way that it cannot be experienced in moral dilemmas. Moral dilemmas are classic cases in which people do, and arguably should, feel morally compromised. Distress is a natural response to a situation in which you are "damned if you do, damned if you don't."[3] To make space for the possibility of moral distress in response to a moral dilemma, we should simply reject the idea that moral distress only results when one is constrained from doing the morally right thing. Moral dilemmas are situations in which there is no (purely) morally right thing to do. Being thrust into a moral dilemma can lead to feelings of distress and moral compromise, loss of well-being, and so on, just as naturally as being faced with a morally right option that one is kept from taking.

Bad Moral Luck

A psychiatrist pushes hard to get his patient to take a medication that he believes will help to address her intractable depression. The patient is initially reluctant, but he eventually persuades her. Two weeks later, she takes an intentional overdose of the medication, which results in her death. The psychiatrist feels terrible about his role in the patient's suicide and wonders whether he did the right thing. However, after reviewing the case, he continues to think that he did exactly what someone in his position should

---

[3] For an influential discussion of moral dilemmas and the appropriateness of one species of distress ("agent-regret"), see Williams (1965).

have done, given the evidence available to him at the time. Even so, he feels great distress about the consequences of his action.

One of the most firmly established beliefs about moral distress is that it is always the result of an individual failing to do the morally right thing where this failing is the result of internal and external constraints. However, it is possible for one to feel morally compromised or tainted even in cases where one is not constrained and one successfully performs what one judges to be the morally best action. One type of case that fits this description involves a certain species of "moral luck."[4] As illustrated in the case just described, sometimes individuals perform what they deem to be the morally best action based on the best information and evidence available to them at the time, without any internal or external constraints. Yet their actions, in conjunction with factors beyond their control, turn out to have morally undesirable consequences (such as the suffering or death of another sentient being or the violation of someone's autonomy or rights). This can lead to feelings of distress. One need not think she should have acted differently. The person may firmly believe that it would have been wrong of her to do otherwise, given what she knew at the time. Still, she may feel terrible that she played a role in bringing about a morally regrettable outcome. This is an instance of distress rooted in the sense that one has been morally compromised, despite the fact that one is not guilty of acting in a wrong or blameworthy manner.

Distress by Association

A nurse at the bedside is responsible for providing clinical care to her patient, who is also a participant in a research study. Based on conversations with the patient, she feels that the patient does not really understand the purpose of the research study and is desperately hoping for any benefit to extend his life. The patient tells her that he did not read the consent form carefully. As the study progresses, the patient's clinical status begins to deteriorate, yet he wants to continue on the study because he thinks it will benefit him. The nurse believes that the patient's continued participation in this research study is morally wrong. She encourages him to meet with the research team to discuss his clinical situation and the purpose and progress of the research, but he is uninterested in doing that. When she mentions her concerns to the research team, they respond that he understands the study well enough and that she should stop worrying. The nurse becomes increasingly troubled by her interactions with this patient. Although she is not part of the research team, she has responsibilities for caring for him and monitoring his clinical status at the bedside where research procedures occur. She feels guilty and distressed about her involvement despite the fact that she has tried very hard to remedy the situation.

This is a second type of case in which one is not subjected to internal or external constraints and one does not fail to do the morally right thing. Distress by association is not grounded in one's own action or omission but in one's association with another party—which might be one or more individuals,

---

[4] The *locus classicus* for this topic is Williams and Nagel (1976). Our present focus is on what is often called "resultant luck," or luck in how things turn out.

or a collective entity.[5] As we are understanding it, distress by association is not essentially a matter of emotional contagion, where distress in one person is triggered by exposure to another's distress. Nor is it a matter of empathetically experiencing the distress that someone else is, or should be, experiencing. Instead, distress by association springs from the sense of being morally compromised due to one's connection with some other party. Perhaps this other party acted immorally with malicious intentions, or acted negligently, or acted morally but with morally disastrous results. Or perhaps this other party has morally condemnable beliefs, attitudes, or motives, without being guilty of *acting* in morally questionable ways. In some cases, distress by association concerns one's membership in a group or organization that has caused a morally undesirable state of affairs, though the responsibility for this does not fall on the distressed individual—or, perhaps, on any particular individual. A doctor might experience distress by association because she works in a health care facility that does not provide adequate care or quality of life for its patients. Here, as in all of the previous cases, it makes good sense to recognize this phenomenon as a species of moral distress. It is distress that arises from a sense of being morally compromised, and it contributes to the sorts of practical problems traditionally associated with moral distress.

A New Definition of Moral Distress

We have argued that our understanding of moral distress should make space for the six types of cases we have discussed. But how should we revise our understanding of moral distress to encompass these cases? What definition of moral distress should we accept? There are countless possibilities, but we offer the following as a promising candidate:

> *Moral distress* $=_{df}$ one or more negative self-directed emotions or attitudes that arise in response to one's perceived involvement in a situation that one perceives to be morally undesirable.

This definition of moral distress has some elements that require clarification. First, it implies that moral distress is a matter of having negative emotions or attitudes that are *self-directed*. These might include self-criticism, guilt, shame, embarrassment, lowered self-esteem, or anger toward oneself or about one's behavior.[6] The restriction to self-directed attitudes is meant to rule out cases in which a person has only other-regarding negative emotions in response to being involved in a morally undesirable situation. Suppose, for instance, that a nurse feels resentment and anger toward a doctor for involving him in the morally questionable treatment of someone who is not his patient. He might

---

[5] This idea is sometimes explored in discussions of "moral taint." See, for instance, Oshana (2006).

[6] These attitudes should spring from a certain appreciation of moral values and not a purely instrumental concern. An egoist or a psychopath might strive to avoid acting immorally solely because it can bring about unwelcome legal and social consequences. If he slips up and does something wrong, he might chastise himself for his stupidity and carelessness. This would not be moral distress.

feel angry about being involved with this case without feeling that *he* is morally compromised by the involvement. If moral compromise is at the heart of moral distress, it seems essential that there are self-directed negative emotions.

Our definition concerns one's perceived *involvement*. This is intentionally vague, allowing for a wide range of ways in which individuals might be related to a morally problematic situation. The involvement might be a matter of having acted or failed to act in certain ways, or having felt or failed to feel certain things. It might be that one has oversight over, and responsibility for, a situation even if one is in no position to intervene. Or it might be that one is simply connected, professionally or personally, to others who are more centrally involved in a morally undesirable situation. Since moral distress is grounded in individuals' perceptions of their involvement, and since individuals will vary quite a bit in the levels and types of involvement that lead them to feel morally compromised, it is ideal for a definition of moral distress to leave space for this variation.

The proposed definition of moral distress refers to situations perceived to be *morally undesirable*. It is notoriously difficult to define "moral." For our purposes, we understand morality to be concerned with the concern and respect that is owed to others. What types of being count as morally relevant "others" (or, we might say, beings with moral status) is a matter of dispute. Variation in people's views about the moral status of a given type of subject—for example, fetuses, animals, brain-dead patients—can help to explain variation in their experience of moral distress. Situations are morally desirable to the extent that due concern and respect to others are shown, and morally undesirable to the extent that they are not. The notion of a morally undesirable situation is meant to be somewhat open-ended. It might include situations that are morally optimal but still morally bad (e.g., where one chooses the lesser of two evils), as well as situations that are morally good but morally nonoptimal (e.g., where one chooses the lesser of two moral goods).

There are some notable contrasts between our proposed definition and the traditional understanding of moral distress. On the traditional view, moral distress is restricted to situations in which, due to constraints, one fails to do what one takes to be the morally right thing. However, cases of moral uncertainty reveal that the restriction to knowledge is too strong. Cases of bad moral luck suggest that moral distress can result from doing what was, in light of the information available at the time, the morally right thing. Cases of moral dilemma show that there need not be a "morally right thing to do." Cases of distress by association show that an individual's own action or omission need not be the source of distress—and, in turn, that the presence of internal or external constraints on action is not essential to moral distress. On our broader definition, moral distress can arise in situations where a person perceives herself to be involved in a morally undesirable situation. This allows for the possibility that an individual does not know what the morally right thing to do is (moral uncertainty), that the individual did the morally best thing though things turned out badly (bad moral luck), that there may not be a morally right thing to do (moral dilemma), or that one's own action is not the issue (distress by association).

Our definition does not place limitations on whether distress occurs at the very moment of one's involvement in a morally undesirable situation, afterward, or both. Unlike the traditional understanding of moral distress, which sees both initial distress and reactive distress as essential elements, our definition allows for the possibility that one does not have one of these. It therefore allows for cases of delayed distress, as well as cases in which one does not experience reactive distress or moral residue (which might happen in cases of mild distress). Interestingly, our definition even allows for the possibility of *anticipatory distress*. If a health care worker believes that, in the future, he or she *will* be involved in a morally undesirable situation, this can lead to distress in the present. This phenomenon may not be all that uncommon. Health care workers who have routinely found themselves entangled in morally undesirable situations can reasonably assume that they will find themselves in such situations in the future.[7] This can be a source of distress in their lives.

Lastly, the traditional understanding of moral distress implies that moral distress only arises from serious violations of one's values and therefore does not acknowledge instances of mild moral distress that, even if not terribly important on their own, can have a significant cumulative impact. In contrast, on our definition even mild forms of negative emotions and attitudes could constitute moral distress. [...]

References

American Association of Critical-Care Nurses. 2008. *Moral distress position statement.* Aliso Viejo, CA: AACN.

Austin, W., Kelecevic, J., Goble, E., and Mekechuk, J. 2009. An overview of moral distress and the paediatric intensive care team. *Nursing Ethics* 16(1): 57–68.

Canadian Nurses Association. 2008. *Code of ethics for registered nurses.* Ottawa, ON, Canada: CNA.

Chen, P. W. 2009. When nurses and doctors can't do the right thing. *New York Times.* February 5. Available at: www.nytimes.com/2009/02/06/health/05chen.html

Corley, M. C. 2002. Nurse moral distress: A proposed theory and research agenda. *Nursing Ethics* 9:636–50.

Corley, M. C., Elswick, R. K., Gorman, M., and Clor, T. 2001. Development and evaluation of a moral distress scale. *Journal of Advanced Nursing* 33(2):250–56.

Epstein, E. G., and Delgado, S. 2010. Understanding and addressing moral distress. *Online Journal of Issues in Nursing* 15(3): 1–12.

Epstein, E. G., and Hamric, A. B. 2009. Moral distress, moral residue, and the crescendo effect. *Journal of Clinical Ethics* 20(4):330–42.

Fourie, C. 2015. Moral distress and moral conflict in clinical ethics. *Bioethics* 29:91–97.

Hamric, A. B. 2014. A case study of moral distress. *Journal of Hospice & Palliative Care Nursing* 16(8):457–63.

---

[7] It is conceivable that anticipatory distress will play some role in the best explanation of the so-called "crescendo effect." See Epstein and Hamric (2009).

Hamric, A. B., and Blackhall, L. J. 2007. Nurse-physician perspectives on the care of dying patients in intensive care units: Collaboration, moral distress, and ethical climate. *Critical Care Medicine* 35(2):422–29.

Hamric, A. B., Borchers, C. T., and Epstein, E. G. 2012. Development and testing of an instrument to measure moral distress in healthcare professionals. *AJOBs Primary Research* 3(2):1–9.

Hanna, D. R. 2004. Moral distress: The state of the science. *Research and Theory for Nursing Practice* 18:73–93.

Jameton, A. 1984. *Nursing practice: The ethical issues.* Prentice Hall.

Jameton, A. 1993. Dilemmas of moral distress: Moral responsibility and nursing practice. *AWHONN's Clinical Issues in Perinatalogy and Women's Health Nursing* 4:542–51.

Kelly, B. 1998. Preserving moral integrity: A follow-up study with new graduate nurses. *Journal of Advanced Nursing* 28:1134–45.

McCarthy, J., and Deady, R. 2008. Moral distress reconsidered. *Nursing Ethics* 15(2):254–62.

Oshana, M. 2006. Moral taint. *Metaphilosophy* 37(3–4):353–75.

Rushton, C. H. 2006. Defining and addressing moral distress. *ACCN Advanced Critical Care* 17(2):161–68.

Ulrich, C. M., Hamric, A., and Grady, C. 2010. Moral distress: A growing problem in the health professions? *Hastings Center Report* 40(1):20–22.

Webster, G. C., and Bayliss, F. 2000. Moral residue. In *Margin of error: The ethics of mistakes in the practice of medicine*, ed. S. B. Rubin and L. Zoloth, 217–30. University Publishing.

Whitehead, P. B., Herbertson, R. K., Hamric, A. B., Epstein, E. G., and Fisher, J. M. 2015. Moral distress among healthcare professionals: Report of an institution-wide survey. *Journal of Nursing Scholarship* 47(2):117–25.

Wilkinson, J. M. 1987–88. Moral distress in nursing practice: Experience and effect. *Nursing Forum* 23(1):16–29.

Williams, B. 1965. Ethical consistency. *Proceedings of the Aristotelian Society, Supplementary* 39:103–24.

Williams, B., and Nagel, T. 1976. Moral luck. *Proceedings of the Aristotelian Society* 50:115–51.

Selection from "Communicating with Integrity"

By Rita Manning and Scott R. Stroud

....

One aspect of integrity that people often overlook is communication. Most people know that communication is a key part of an *effective* person's repertoire, but few consider the *ethical* dimensions of communication.[1] Being able to make your point in any given interaction is an important skill, but having the right orientation toward that communicative situation is what truly instills integrity and moral worth into that action. It is said that Mussolini was a violent dictator, but that he made the trains run on time—effective and ethical are two qualities that obviously do not always go together. In this [reading], we hope to introduce you to the ethical aspects of communication: that is, how we can communicate with integrity.

There are two things involved with ethical communication. First, in communicating with others you must respect them as persons with moral value. Second, in order to transform your environment into one that is more ethical, you must be able to communicate your values to others in an articulate and persuasive way. Part of communication is getting your own ideas across. The other part of it is listening, reading, and learning from others.

Though we all pay lip service to the idea of communication as a two-way street, we too often see only our side of it. This is so pervasive that in English we don't even have a word that captures two-way communication. Instead we speak of "speakers," "listeners," "audience," "writers," "readers." It's always important to keep in mind that communication is a complex activity; we listen and we speak.

---

[1] For an empirical report on the importance of communication in the world of business, see Jerry L. Winsor, Dan B. Curtis, and Ronald D. Stephens, "National Preferences in Business and Communication Education: A Survey Update," *Journal of the Association for Communication Administration* 3 (1997), 174.

Doing Things with Words

Deborah Tannen has described a difficulty that often arises in conversations between men and women.[2] If a woman tries to talk to her partner about something that is upsetting, he typically responds in one of three ways: by staring at her with a blank expression on his face, by giving advice, or by asking what he should do about it. The woman may feel frustrated by this response, because she really just wanted someone to understand what she was feeling and to sympathize. What is happening here is that men and women often do not have the same idea of the purpose of the communication. Such misunderstandings are common, and they frustrate many attempts to communicate. It stands to reason that in order to communicate with integrity, it is necessary to become more aware of some of the things we can do with communication.

One of the things we can do with communication is inform. I give you information that you did not previously have. This is a pretty straightforward interaction. Other types of communication are usually more complex.

The second thing we can do is misinform. There are two ways to misinform. First, I might want to give you accurate information, and I give you information that I think is accurate, but it turns out that my information is incorrect. The second way to misinform is to make what looks like an informing communication, but with the intention to mislead the listener. In either case, I succeed at misinforming if my listener believes what I say.

We can also use words to inquire. My inquiry is successful if I ask for information and you understand my request. You can then choose whether to inform or misinform me, and I can choose whether to accept or reject what you say.

We can use communication to build relationships. We can seek reassurance, and we can reassure. We can seek understanding, and we can convey that we do understand. Or we can use language to torpedo relationships. We can criticize, alienate, and create unhealthy competition. Good leaders understand the power of language to sustain good relationships and they use it consciously.

Relationships are not simply dyadic—that is, they are not just between two people—but we will start with this type of relationship to illustrate how we can use language to build up a relationship. Georg Hegel was a nineteenth-century German philosopher who described relationships as crucial factors in our self-understanding.[3] As Aristotle pointed out, humans are essentially social creatures. We develop our sense of self through interactions with others. No matter how healthy your sense of self is, it will be nurtured or damaged in your interactions with others. If you are constantly criticized, you will begin to doubt yourself. If you are excessively praised, you will begin to distrust the messenger. Hegel's great insight was to see that this dynamic goes both ways, even when there

---

[2] Deborah Tannen, *You Just Don't Understand: Women and Men in Communication* (New York: Harper, 2001).

[3] G.W.F. Hegel, "B: Self Consciousness," in *The Phenomenology of Spirit* (originally published 1807) (Oxford: Oxford University Press, 1979).

is a great disparity of power. An example will help to make this clear. Let's consider the relationship between Jay and Howard.

Jay is Howard's employee. Howard is very hard on Jay. He expects Jay to always be available and to anticipate his every whim. Jay manages to keep his job because he satisfies Howard's expectations, even though Howard never acknowledges this. Indeed, Howard only comments on Jay's work when Jay has made a mistake. We can see how Howard is damaging Jay. The lack of recognition for a job well done diminishes Jay's sense of accomplishment, and Howard's criticism damages Jay's self-esteem. Because of the unreasonable expectations, Jay is much more aware of Howard's needs than his own. As Hegel would point out, Howard is also diminished by their interaction. Howard's sense of self-mastery is undermined by his continued reliance on Jay. Since Jay feels no sense of joy in their interactions, Howard never gets a sense of himself as a pleasant human being. The longer they are locked in this interaction, the worse their own self-understandings will be.

Let's look at another case. Sara is an administrative assistant who works for Roberto. Roberto makes a point of respecting boundaries. He never asks Sara to do more than her job description requires, and he stays on top of his own tasks. He is quick to complement her on a job well done, and he is sensitive to her life outside the company. Sara feels valued, and Roberto feels competent and fair.

There are two important things to keep in mind here. The first is that we all influence and are influenced by the people with whom we interact. The second is that relationships are not static. They will continue to grow either negatively or positively. If you want to be an effective and ethical leader and a healthy and happy person, you must reflect on your relationships. Try to establish and nurture positive interactions and limit negative ones. Think about the enormous power of words to create and sustain relationships, for good or ill.

Just about everyone has been to a family get-together or a class reunion where all those in attendance seem committed to outshining each other. While on the surface it seems as though people are just trading information about their lives, they are really trying to one-up each other. Everyone has the most accomplished kids, the best job, and the highest compensation package. Here we see the power of communication to express hidden agendas. Some of the most common hidden agendas are displays of status and displays of emotion. When we use communication to display status, we are often trying to show power over and contempt for others. Conversely, we might be showing our submission to others or trying to assert our equality in the face of a challenge. We can also use communication to display emotion. We raise our voices and use criticism to display anger; we lower our voice and our eyes to express disinterest.

Communication in Leadership

Human communication is amazingly fluid and effective at doing many things. If you want to be an effective and ethical leader, you must first notice what you can do with words and then communicate thoughtfully and deliberately. Ethical leadership is more effective leadership because it embraces honest, informative, and supportive communication.

Communication must be honest because it is not possible for us to continue in dishonest communication. You might think you are not going to speak out about what you view as unfair treatment, but you will communicate this in other ways if you don't communicate it in a clear, deliberate manner. You will communicate it to the wrong person, at the wrong time, or in an inappropriate way. Communication for leaders must involve sharing information because leaders cannot succeed without loyal and committed followers who are able to carry out their tasks, and the followers cannot carry out their tasks if they are burdened by incomplete and inaccurate information. Finally, communication for leaders must build trust. No team activity can succeed without the full and generous cooperation of all members of the team, and this full and generous cooperation cannot take place without an atmosphere of trust.

Orientation in Communication

When one is in a role of leadership, one has ample opportunities to communicate with other people. Indeed, communication seems to be necessitated not so much by leadership, but by human nature itself. As Aristotle noted long ago, humans are social animals. It is through our community and communication that we define others, the world, and ourselves. Language, and the ways we use it, have a world-shaping power in that they let us manipulate the world or offer a way for our social world to change us. For instance, the skin color of an individual can become the grounds for radical hate—simply because of hateful stories and narratives that locate that "group" of people as lower in the "chain of being" than the individual making the judgment.[4]

What is of importance at this early stage of discussion is to draw attention to how our communication *orients* us to the world. Besides pointing out what is of importance, the way we use words also tells something about how we approach the world. In the world, leaders must communicate. The choice that remains deals with what type of *orientation* that person in the role of leadership brings to his or her communicative activities with other people. Each person has a particular orientation to how he or she views the use of language in communication. Such an orientation answers such questions as:

> How is the other person to be treated?
> What is the goal of communication?
> How are the participants in communication related to each other?

This orientation exists in all who communicate, though the answers to these questions may be more unconscious than overt. For instance, say Tom goes into a business meeting to convince others

---

[4] Much of the power that hate groups have derives from their use of religious and secular stories (involving language) that include the receptive listener as a member; thus, some individuals see themselves as fulfilling certain prophecies, avidly defending themselves against a conspiratorial government, etc.

that a particular plan of action would be beneficial. Tom makes a powerful presentation about why this plan should be adopted by the company, and the others leave thinking he is correct in his assessment of the merits of the plan. What was the purpose of Tom's speech, and how did he interact with the other participants in this instance of communication? Perhaps Tom felt that his overriding goal was to get the others to believe him. This, however, betrays his orientation toward this instance of communication—the goal of the communication was to get what he wanted.

Although it may seem like Tom was treating others with respect, this foundational orientation toward achieving the desired end of persuasion may have compromised the value he placed on the other participants. To extend the example, imagine a situation where the listeners do not find the speech compelling. To what extent would the speaker go to get them to agree with his or her view? What would provide limits to this quest to get others to agree with one's ideas, wishes, or proposals? As you can see, one's orientation toward communication, and toward the other participants involved, is crucial in an interaction, and understanding orientation is crucial to examining issues of integrity in leadership. While a variety of ethical guidelines have been given, two competing orientations will be described below to help illustrate the foundation that a leader with integrity carries into communicative situations.

Persuasion-Centered Orientation.

One extremely prevalent approach to communication in Western society can be labeled the "persuasion-centered" orientation. This is the orientation that most individuals are exposed to and the one they often unknowingly assimilate. This conception of communication comes from a long line of theories that owe allegiance to Aristotle, who stated that rhetoric (communication) was "the power to observe the persuasiveness of which any particular matter admits."[5] According to this orientation, the purpose of communication is to achieve something *the communicator* wants—thus, it becomes a tool, as in Aristotle's formulation.

This orientation, however, is not without its flaws. It can easily lead to an unethical focus on the self at the exclusion of other people and their interests; it can also lead to denying the intrinsic worth of communication. How these two limitations become evident will be illustrated in a moment. What is of importance now is to unearth the presuppositions behind this view of communication. We will assume that those who hold the persuasion-centered view are committed to the idea of persuasion, even if they are not aware of it.

The persuasion-centered view is based upon some key presuppositions about how the world works and how people relate to each other.[6] First, it assumes that communication is composed of *atomic individuals pursuing their own desires and goals.* When one speaks, one is trying to get what one wants, and each individual is portrayed as separate from each other individual in terms of what each wants

---

[5] Aristotle, *The Art of Rhetoric,* translated by H. C. Lawson-Tancred (New York: Penguin Books, 1991), 74.
[6] The ideas in what follows can be seen in a slightly different form in Scott R. Stroud, "Tempering Public Speaking Pedagogy with Insights from the *Bhagavad Gita,*" *Journal of the Wisconsin Communication Association* 32 (2001), 56–64.

and how it is to be achieved. Often these individuals are seen as competing in communication. For example, say that in Tom's business meeting, there was some disagreement about the appropriate course of action. The communicators can be seen as each pursuing his or her own desires and employing the communicative tools needed to achieve them (for instance, a polished presentation/speech).

In addition, under this orientation, *ethical norms must recognize this separate and competitive nature of reality*. The audience and the speaker are ultimately separate, so what is often termed as "ethical" communication is that which avoids negative reactions from these separate individuals—ethics becomes tied to effectively achieving one's goals. As our intuitions tell us in the case of the Mussolini example, effectiveness and achieving one's goals do not always translate into ethical behavior or integrity of leadership.

Third, the goal of communication under this orientation *is to affect the world—to adapt it to one's desires*. Under the persuasion-centered orientation, the speaker is an individual who sets out to change the actions or behaviors of some audience. He or she may want to make the audience believe a message, agree with certain ideas, feel particular emotions, have a good impression of the speaker, and so on. Communication is conceived of as a tool for "fixing" the world; what is "broken" about the world, of course, is everything that is not in line with the speaker's desires, wants, and needs.

Lastly, this orientation toward communication holds that *actions that are not effective in reaching one's goal are not rationally advisable*. One speaks solely to accomplish a specific purpose, and this goal must be realized in order for the speech to be valuable; otherwise, one would do something else. With this view, if Tom in the previous example knew that his speech would not be successful in changing the minds of the other people present, he would have chosen another tactic to achieve the goal (to get a certain plan put into action), or may not even have proposed the plan at all.

Exercise 3.2.1

Think about a time when you were treated badly by another person in the way that he or she communicated with you. How were you treated? Did you feel valued? Why or why not? What could the other person have done to make you feel more valued? What was the other person's goal in the interaction with you?

Invitational Orientation.

Another orientation to communication is labeled the "invitational orientation."[7] In contrast to persuasion-centered communication, which involves domination and control, invitational communication

---

[7] S. K. Foss, and C. L. Griffin, "Beyond Persuasion: A Proposal for an Invitational Rhetoric," *Communication Monographs* 62 (1995), 2–18; S. K. Foss and K. A. Foss, *Inviting Transformation: Presentational Speaking for a Changing World* (Prospect Heights, Ill.: Waveland, 1994); S. K. Foss and K. A. Foss, *Instructor's Manual to Accompany Inviting Transformation: Presentational Speaking for a Changing World* (Prospect Heights, Ill.: Waveland, 2000).

draws upon fundamental values such as "equality, immanent value, and self-determination"[8] in informing theoretical commitments. This orientation is predicated on *openness* by the speaker. The invitational communicator does not see communication as a tool to bend others to one's will, but as a way of *presenting* oneself through communicating one's experiences, opinions, and views, and of *inviting* the responses of the other participants in the communication. This fundamental openness to others seeks to *invite,* not force; it welcomes the transformation of both the audience member and the speaker but does not try to force any transformation upon one party or the other.

Invitational rhetoric also holds certain presuppositions, many of which are opposed to the persuasion-centered view. Initially, this perspective holds that *individuals are interrelated and interdependent.* Each person resides in a complex web of relationships and dependencies that cannot be escaped. For instance, one depends on others for the production, packaging, safety, and quality of one's food. Additionally, the choices that a farmer makes concerning his or her livelihood affects other people in important ways—those who work on the farm, those who compete against it in the market, and those who end up consuming the food it produces. Thus, the invitational perspective recognizes that individuals are not separate entities trying to achieve their own goals, but interdependent beings pursuing complementary goals, common objectives, and similar interests.

This linkage of individuals also means that *individuals involved in communication have intrinsic worth.* Many ethical systems have laid out guidelines and justifications for why people should be treated with respect in instances of communication. The newest twist on this idea comes from feminist theorists, who often find that individuals are radically different and unique and that as such they hold intrinsic value that is separate from any value they may have in achieving certain goals, ends, and the like.[9] But this view has a long and respected history. Some deontological (duty-based) systems find that humans are intrinsically valuable because of essential similarities—for instance, Immanuel Kant found that individuals all have the same faculties of reason and the moral law which derives from it.[10] Eastern texts, such as the *Bhagavad Gita* and the *Astavakra Gita,* postulate that all humans are valuable because they are all part of one big Self, or consciousness.[11] The point behind all of these theories is that humans have a value that goes above and beyond their usefulness to any person or purpose. Thus, in communication, participants are equals and not "pawns" to be moved around as if they were game pieces.

The invitational orientation also holds that *the goal of communication is to increase free interaction and transformative opportunities.* Persuasion as coercion is not seen as allowable in this view—communication that relies on tactics to scare or cower participants into siding with the communicator are not

---

[8] Foss and Griffin, *Beyond Persuasion,* 4.

[9] Ibid.; K. A. Foss, S. K. Foss, and C. L. Griffin, *Feminist Rhetorical Theories* (Thousand Oaks, Calif.: Sage Publications, 1999).

[10] See Immanuel Kant, *Foundations of the Metaphysics of Morals,* translated by L. W. Beck (New York: Macmillan, 1985); Immanuel Kant, *Critique of Practical Reason,* translated by L. W. Beck (Upper Saddle River, N.J.: Prentice Hall, 1993).

[11] Eliot Deutsch, *The Bhagavad Gita: Translated, with Introduction and Critical Essays.* (New York: University Press of America, 1968); S. Nityaswarupananda, trans., *Astavakra Samhita,* 10th ed. (Calcutta, India: Trio Process, 1998).

methods of communication that respect others as equals. Instead, the participants in communication should see a discussion or speech as a way of inviting transformation in others as they offer their perspectives, views, personal experiences, and so on. The speaker is not trying to control or change the other person. The offering that he or she gives to the others in the form of a speech includes openness to the experiences and views of other people and does not assume that other people are objects to be manipulated. Because the same type of openness is hoped for in the audience, certain external conditions are looked upon as favorable, since they can facilitate audience offerings. External conditions for audience openness are optimal when the speaker creates a *safe* environment for interaction, recognizes the intrinsic *value* of the audience members, and makes all parties feel *free* to interact.[12]

These conditions, if fostered by the rhetor, can *invite* audience transformation through open interaction—in other words, by not being treated as objects to be manipulated, the audience members feel valued as individuals and can open up to the views of the speaker and of the other audience members. It is this open flow of ideas that affirms the self-worth of all involved, preempts defensive reactions to differing messages, and clears the way for actual change to occur—change that the participants agree with and freely choose.

One last commitment can be added to this picture of the invitational orientation—*the value of communication is not contained solely in its consequences.* [...] Here it suffices to say that "ineffective" communication is often morally praiseworthy. There will be times in one's life when duty, position, or hope may compel one to take a stand, to speak out on a certain issue to individuals who probably will not listen or change. The invitational orientation recognizes that leaders will often have to stand *against* overwhelming odds, and they will not always be assured of achieving desired results.

You may be alone, facing a hostile audience, but you may feel that you *need* to speak your mind and oppose what you find is a grievous harm to tolerance, diversity, or some other principle you believe in. You deliver your perspective eloquently, and with respect for others who hold opposite opinions. If the crowd heeds your invitation to temper their actions, so much the better for you and your desires. If they do not, your action still exhibited integrity and honor. Part of this integrity comes from the fact that you did not silence yourself as someone who was not equal in "voice" to the others.

Exercise 3.2.2

Recall a situation where you felt valued as a person through the way another person talked with you. What did that person do that made you feel valued and important? How did that person see you as a participant in the conversation? What was his or her goal in that conversation?

---

[12] Foss and Griffin, "Beyond Persuasion."

Recall a time when you spoke to a boss, a fellow employee, or a group of colleagues in a work-related situation that could have called for either the persuasion-centered approach or the invitational approach to communication. Which orientation did you choose? What choices and strategies did you use in the way that you spoke? How would these have been different if you had picked the other orientation?

Communicating at Full Potential

If one believes that the invitational orientation is superior to the persuasion-centered orientation (because it recognizes the worth of individuals, allows for the interrelations between individuals, and gives actions values even when they may not be successful), does that mean that one need not work hard at preparing and delivering a persuasive or compelling message or speech?

The answer is simple. With the construction of a message, one should attempt to honor or value one's audience, one's ideas, and oneself. If you truly care about an *audience*, or group of people to be addressed, then the way you prepare and construct that message should reflect this respect. Honoring the audience means presenting them with the best message or speech you can muster. When you are faced with a decision about whether to present the audience with a worthy, polished message or not, this is an ethical choice, since it highlights the issue of the respect you give to your audience and the value that you place on them. In addition, if you truly care about your *ideas*, then you will place them in the most compelling light possible and present a strong argument. If you care about these ideas enough to share them, why slight them with shoddy wording or distracting delivery? Honoring the ideas means preparing a speech worthy of their importance both to you and to the audience. You can also honor *yourself* in and through your message. If you construct a speech on important ideas and you do not do the ideas justice, you not only fail to respect the ideas but also demonstrate that you do not care much about how committed you seem toward those ideas.

[…] The way you go about writing, delivering, and even listening to prepared speeches is part of what makes you a leader with integrity. Each person literally can have a "voice" in our society, but it takes practice to express that voice to your fullest potential. The ability to stand and speak up for what you believe is important merits communication that is eloquent, prepared, and worthy of the ideas presented. Not every kind of speech is formal, or on serious topics. But even in more conversational settings, one's communication can be carried out with integrity. In both serious and more ordinary contexts, communication involves respecting yourself, respecting important ideas and values, and listening attentively and respectfully to others. Thus, *effective* communication and *ethical* communication join in actual practice. […]

Moral Courage

By Matthew Pianalto

Eastern Kentucky University

··

> *"It is hard to be brave. It is hard to know what bravery is."*
> —Tim O'Brien, *If I Die in a Combat Zone* (1973)

Introduction

Courage is among the most universally recognized human virtues. It involves mastery of one of the basic human emotions, fear, so as to endure and overcome danger for the sake of some good. Often, courage involves self-sacrifice, the risk of life and limb to protect or defend others. Brave people keep the rest of us safe.[1] The value of courage reflects the interdependence of the individual and society: a good society needs brave people to uphold its values and principles and to defend its territory and interests, but good people sometimes need to be brave in order to hold others within the community accountable and to challenge social norms or habits that are not good.

Although courage is sometimes thinly defined as knowingly engaging in a dangerous situation in order to achieve a desirable goal, this thin definition fails to distinguish courage from problematic character traits such as recklessness and rashness. Moral courage involves choosing one's battles wisely and contending with the situation in an appropriate manner. The need for proportionality in acting with courage implies that not every way of standing firm with the "courage of conviction" is admirable or good. After all, people with vicious goals or false beliefs may also seem to possess the courage of conviction. Morally arrogant and self-righteous people may be bold and loud, but

---

[1] In what follows, I will use *courage* and *bravery* interchangeably since they convey the same basic idea.

such bluster is not the same thing as moral courage.[2] People who are too sure of themselves and too demeaning of others risk judging and acting in ways that are thoughtless and unfair. The morally courageous person stands firm but is also not afraid to listen and learn. They are not afraid to recognize even their rivals as fellow human beings, with whom discourse is possible. This involves facing others as *moral agents* rather than treating them merely as obstacles or beasts.

Two Kinds of Courage

In 1968, a college-bound Tim O'Brien was drafted into the United States Army and would be sent to fight alongside many other draftees in the Vietnam War.[3] When he learned his draft number had been called, O'Brien faced a moral dilemma because he believed that the war was wrong. He contemplated becoming a draft dodger and fleeing to Canada. Dodging the draft seemed cowardly, but fighting in an unjust war did not seem like a particularly brave alternative.

O'Brien reflected on Socrates's refusal to flee Athens after he had been sentenced to death. Charged with impiety and corrupting the youth, Socrates maintained his innocence throughout his trial and argued that the real reason he had been brought to court was because of his commitment to philosophical questioning and discussion. He lived by the maxim that "the unexamined life is not worth living" and argued that it would be worse for him to abandon this moral commitment to philosophical dialogue than to be killed by those who wished to silence him.[4] In taking this stand, Socrates demonstrated moral courage.

He later reaffirms this commitment when his friend Crito offers to help him escape from prison and avoid execution. Socrates reasons that escaping would contradict his earlier arguments; it would be a failure of integrity. Furthermore, Socrates suggests that by appearing in court, he had entered into an agreement with the city to accept the outcome of the trial. In a sense, this is part of the social contract to which he agreed by continuing to live and philosophize in Athens over his seventy years.

Although O'Brien's situation is not quite like Socrates's predicament, it is understandable that he might think of being drafted into the army during the Vietnam conflict as tantamount to an unjust death sentence. Even so, Socrates remained brave when sentenced to death. O'Brien decided ultimately to go to war rather than flee to Canada, perhaps out of a sense of social responsibility similar to that of Socrates. Nevertheless, he feared that he made this choice mainly because he was afraid of being seen as a coward by his family and friends.

O'Brien's dilemma highlights the tension between social responsibility and personal conviction and between two different forms of courage. On the one hand, there is the *traditional or physical courage* of the brave warrior who faces death and fights with boldness against a dangerous foe. On the

---

[2] See John S. Murray, "Moral Courage in Healthcare: Acting Ethically Even in the Presence of Risk," *OJIN: The Online Journal of Issues in Nursing* 15(3) (2010), Manuscript 2.

[3] Tim O'Brien, *If I Die in a Combat Zone, Box Me Up and Ship Me Home*, Dell (1973).

[4] As related in two works by Plato, the *Apology* and *Crito*.

other hand, there is the *moral courage* of those who stand firm in the name of some moral cause or principle in political, professional, or other social contexts. This is the kind of courage exhibited by whistleblowers and those who refuse to follow unjust orders. In O'Brien's case, perhaps it would have been morally courageous to refuse to fight, even though he might thereby be suspected of physical cowardice and selfishness, of being afraid to fight (and die) for his country. This is part of the risk that the morally courageous person takes—being ridiculed, rejected, and punished for taking a stand. As the trial and death of Socrates illustrates, moral courage can be just as risky as physical courage.

However, just as refusing to fight or follow orders is not always cowardice, it is perhaps not always brave to risk your life or reputation for the sake of principle. There is a difference between being courageous and being reckless, rash, or foolish. Aristotle says, "whoever stands firm against the right things and fears the right things, for the right end, in the right way, at the right time, and is correspondingly confident, is the brave person."[5] This account suggests that true courage must get many things right, which would explain why O'Brien finds it so hard to know what bravery is.

Courage Through Thick and Thin

Aristotle's account of courage is morally *thick* in that all true courage is also *moral* courage. That is, Aristotle stipulates that courage is only a virtue if it aims toward what is right and good. Thus, a dangerous act can only be properly described as courageous if it has a truly moral aim and is done "in the right way, at the right time," and so on. Courage is a *mean*—a state that is in between—both cowardice on the one hand and recklessness and rashness on the other. This makes courage complex because it requires not only mastery of fear and danger but also moral and practical wisdom: to be brave, it is not enough to be able to face danger. One also has to know what is right and when and how facing danger will achieve what is right in a way that is itself morally acceptable. Some critics object that Aristotle's view makes courage too complicated or that it conflates courage and other virtues like justice, temperance, and wisdom. Common sense, so the objection goes, tells us that people are sometimes quite brave even though they are not the wisest or even the fairest people.

Unlike Aristotle's account, courage is sometimes defined much more thinly, simply as the intentional undertaking of a dangerous course of action to achieve some valued end.[6] Thin accounts present two basic conditions for courage: (1) the awareness of danger or fear and (2) a valued goal. These accounts are *thin* in that they do not stipulate that the "end" pursued by the courageous person is necessarily right or good, only that it is valued subjectively. The first condition (danger or fear) can also be treated thinly: courage is needed any time one *believes* that a situation is dangerous (or experiences fear).

---

[5] Aristotle, *Nicomachean Ethics*, trans. Terence Irwin, Hackett (1999), Book 3, Chapter 7.
[6] For an example of a thin definition of courage, see A. Silke, "Courage in Dark Places: Reflections on Terrorist Psychology," *Social Research* 71(1) (2004): 177–98.

This gives us the following idea: a person acts with courage if they intentionally engage in a course of action that they *believe* is dangerous for a reason that they *believe* to be right or good.[7]

This account of courage may capture core aspects of the psychology of courage, and it has the advantage of making it possible to recognize the courage of someone whose values or motivations differ from one's own. What counts for courage on thin accounts is the *belief* that one's action is both dangerous and right. It would seem provincial, close-minded, and even arrogant to hold that only people who share our values can be brave. Even so, the thin account may seem *too* thin to align with our sense that courage is difficult and excellent. The thin characterization of courage seems to do too little to distinguish it from other bold, daring, or fearless conditions that can do more harm than good.

Aristotle recognizes that we are not all equally fearful of the same things. Some people have intense, if irrational, phobias, and there is a sense in which it takes some courage for such people to face and overcome their fears. However, some things are dangerous for all people, and, thus, reasonably feared. Someone who is insensitive to real danger is not so much brave as insanely fearless—and such a condition is apt to lead to rash and reckless risk-taking. Aristotle would add that there are some things that we *ought* to fear, such as doing something morally foolish or becoming a bad person. Furthermore, if we make courage entirely subjective, we encounter some potentially counterintuitive results such as that moral fanatics and terrorists who kill innocent people for the sake of their causes appear to count as brave even though many people are reticent to apply the badge of courage to such people. On the one hand, we might say that such people serve as a reminder that courage is not always good.[8] On the other hand, we might want to reconsider Aristotle's thicker position that *courage* is the name of a *human excellence* that we should reserve for actions that are dangerous but genuinely well-chosen and, thus, deserving of our praise and admiration.

Courage, Cowardice, and Recklessness

Shortly after the terrorist attacks in the United States on September 11, 2001, the political commentator Bill Maher sparked outrage and ultimately lost his job at ABC by making the following comment about the suicide bombers: "Staying in the airplane when it hits the building—say what you want about it, it's not cowardly." Similarly, Susan Sontag wrote in *The New Yorker*, "Whatever may be said of the perpetrators of Tuesday's slaughter, they were not cowards." These provocative comments were a response to the broad refrain that the suicide bombers *were* cowards because their actions killed thousands of innocent people. According to this latter way of thinking, only cowards would adopt such underhanded means of attacking their enemies.

Even if we find Maher and Sontag's remarks offensive, it seems clear that neither of them were saying anything obviously false. Sacrificing your life for a moral, religious, or political cause is not the

---

[7] See, e.g., James Wallace, *Virtues and Vices*, Cornell University Press (1978), 78ff.
[8] See Per Bauhn, *The Value of Courage*, Nordic Academic Press (2003), 89.

characteristic behavior of a coward. In a sense, the terrorists had the courage of their convictions, and I imagine that members of Al Qaeda thought of these men as brave. *They* believed they were doing the right thing. If we stick with a thin account of courage, then it seems like the suicide bombers were brave. An exception would be if they had somehow been coerced into hijacking and crashing the airplane and, so, were acting out of a fear of punishment for refusing to follow orders: that would be a kind of cowardice, or at least a kind of servile obedience. Nevertheless, if we suppose that the hijackers had freely internalized the cause and recognized the dangers and costs of their actions, then they were acting with courage in the thin sense.

However, it is worth noticing that neither Maher nor Sontag were quite willing to say that the hijackers were *brave*, and Aristotle's approach helps to clarify that there are ways of being "not cowards" that are also not genuinely brave. Recall that Aristotle holds that the brave person aims at a noble goal but also pursues that goal "in the right way." One way of understanding this criterion is pragmatic or practical: brave people adopt means to their ends that are effective. Trying to explain to a bear why he should not eat my children for lunch is not an effective means of stopping a bear from preying upon tasty children. However, given Aristotle's commitment to characterizing each virtue in such a manner that it coheres with other virtues so that courageous actions will also be just, wise, and temperate, we should assume that Aristotle is not just thinking about effectiveness when he says that brave acts must be done "in the right way." Rather, Aristotle is suggesting that a brave action must be moral both in its *end* (or goal) and in the *means* adopted to realize that end.

In the case of the hungry bear, my goal is to protect my family. This is a perfectly noble goal to have in a dangerous situation. Suppose, however, that I spot a nearby child who is not my own and push that child in the direction of the oncoming bear. In effect, I am using this child as a kind of human shield, and this may be an effective way to protect *my* family. Is this brave? It seems not, insofar as I'm taking advantage of a power disparity between myself and the child and deciding for them that they will be the bear's next meal. In the language of Kantian ethics, I am using this child merely as a means without respecting the child as an end. I have achieved my goal in a dangerous situation but done so in a heartless and inhumane way.

We can draw similar conclusions about the 9/11 attackers. They were neither cowardly nor brave because their attack on innocent people and their use of full passenger planes as missiles involved using those innocents as means to their own terroristic ends. One way to think about this is that it seems *reckless* to kill all those innocent people in the process of taking down their military targets, and this recklessness becomes a kind of injustice, too.

Someone might suggest that from the perspective of the terrorists, none of their victims were innocent: they were *infidels*, and, thus, complicit in the corruption and immorality of their society. But this doesn't really solve the problem because even if we granted this as a perspectival truth for the terrorists, it is a reckless thing to believe. On the one hand, even among Muslims, the views of the terrorists are extreme and widely rejected; perhaps the end of the matter is that it is just *false* for them to think that infidels may be sacrificed when convenient for their cause. On the other hand, we could point out that there was no realistic way for the terrorists to know who else was on the plane with them or in the buildings that they destroyed. Maybe many of the victims were not infidels.[9] However you cut it, the terrorists made a dubious decision that innocent people deserved to die—either as collateral damage or as part of the very message they wished to send to the world—and it is entirely unclear what right they had to make such a decision. That they sacrificed their own lives, too, should not obscure the basic indecency of using innocent people in this way. Put perhaps too simply, they were not fighting fair.

Bravely Facing Others

[...] I argued that moral courage requires facing others, including our adversaries, as moral agents.[10] The basic idea is that there is an important difference between bravely facing some merely physical obstacle or threat such as a burning building, a hungry bear, or a cancer diagnosis and taking a brave moral stand against other thinking and reasoning beings like ourselves. We cannot reason with fires, bears, or cancer even though we can endure these obstacles bravely in order to achieve some noble goal. On the other hand, when we take a stand against other people, the moral agency we share makes it possible to pursue our ends in ways that are unavailable when we are battling against the forces of nature. We can engage in moral reasoning and judgment with each other. This makes it possible to resolve moral conflicts and mistakes without physical force.

Since the brave person is not reckless and because physical fighting is risky, the brave person has reasons to seek dialogical rather than combative resolutions to moral conflicts. One reason is prudential or self-interested: choose your battles wisely; don't take unnecessary or stupid risks. But the other reason is moral: it is a matter of respect for other people that we treat them like moral reasoners rather than as irrational brutes or unthinking things. Amélie Oksenberg Rorty worries that traditional or physical courage tends to objectify the threats that must be overcome.[11] But this a morally dangerous attitude to adopt toward other people since we risk treating them as mere things rather than as fellow persons or moral agents.

One might object that the requirement that brave people face their human adversaries as moral agents puts the brave person at a disadvantage: often, we need brave people to stand up to bullies and bad actors who themselves are not treating others ethically. We don't need courage to talk to reasonable people but rather to *fight* against people who are unreasonable! There are two things to say about this. First, when our safety is under direct threat, self-defense is justified. However, many

---

[9] Indeed, there were Muslims among the victims of the 9/11 attacks. See David Usborne, "Collateral Damage: The Forgotten Muslim Victims of 11 September 2001," *The Independent*, Thursday, October 11, 2001, https://www.independent.co.uk/news/world/americas/collateral-damage-5363427.html.

[10] Matthew Pianalto, "Moral Courage and Facing Others," *International Journal of Philosophical Studies* 20(2) (2012): 165–184.

[11] Amélie Oksenberg Rorty, "Two Faces of Courage," *Philosophy* 61: 236 (1986), 151–171. See also Peter Olsthoorn, "Courage in the Military: Physical and Moral," *Journal of Military Ethics* 6:4 (2007), 270–279.

instances of moral courage involve *accepting* a threat to one's own safety and security in order to achieve some other goal. Socrates could have saved his life by fleeing prison or perhaps by conducting his defense speech differently while on trial, but either of these actions would have compromised his moral goal and, thus, his integrity. His mission was not to live but to persuade his fellow Athenians that philosophical questioning is vital for the intellectual and spiritual well-being of the city. But he could not pursue *that* mission without addressing the jurors at his trial as reasoning moral agents. His moral stand required that he accept exposure to the violent response of those who were not persuaded by his arguments.

Moral courage of this kind is rooted in a hope for change through reasoning and persuasion rather than through physical coercion or the crushing of one's enemies. Centuries later, Martin Luther King, Jr., cited the example of Socrates in his "Letter from Birmingham Jail" in order to defend his own work as a "gadfly" for the cause of racial desegregation:

> Just as Socrates felt that it was necessary to create a tension in the mind so that individuals could rise from the bondage of myths and half-truths to the unfettered realm of creative analysis and objective appraisal, so must we see the need for nonviolent gadflies to create the kind of tension in society that will help men rise from the dark depths of prejudice and racism to the majestic heights of understanding and brotherhood.[12]

Notice that King hopes for *understanding and brotherhood*—that is his conception of victory. But we can only achieve such goods by facing others *as* one moral agent to another and by fostering the idea that we share a moral community with each other despite our differences and the moral failings to which we are all vulnerable.

Moral courage, thus, involves striking a balance between the willingness to stand alone against unethical behavior and a desire to build a community of justice and between confidence in our moral vision and the intellectual humility that enables us to listen to and learn from others. William Ian Miller quips that "moral courage is *lonely* courage" because those who take brave moral stands often find themselves isolated or in a minority.[13] Humans typically crave belonging, and speaking out against workplace misconduct, social injustices against minorities, or other divisive moral issues may put us at risk of becoming social pariahs. However, Miller's observation is not the whole truth because when one person demonstrates the courage to speak out or stand up, others will often follow, inspired by the brave person's example. In such cases, moral courage is the first step toward collaborative reform and social transformation.

---

[12] Martin Luther King, Jr., "Letter from Birmingham Jail" (1963), https://www.africa.upenn.edu/Articles_Gen/Letter_Birmingham.html.
[13] William Ian Miller, *The Mystery of Courage*, Harvard University Press (2000), 255.

Conclusion

Moral courage involves acting for a moral cause despite the presence of danger in a way that respects the moral agency of others. Because courage is a virtue, it is something to which we should aspire. Are we ever *obligated* to act in a brave manner? This is a difficult question because actions that risk significant self-sacrifice may seem to be *supererogatory*—above and beyond the call of duty. Nevertheless, because courage has both personal value in enabling us to act with integrity in difficult situations and social value in promoting a moral community, perhaps we can say that we are each obliged to devote some time to cultivating this trait.

Debra Comer and Michael Schwartz suggest that we can begin by studying exemplars of moral courage, who model speaking up or taking stand in ethically difficult situations, and that such activities can promote the development of moral courage in a classroom setting.[14] Others have argued that moral courage cannot be taught in a classroom because classrooms are designed to be safe spaces for learning, but courage requires risk.[15] There is something to this worry, and Aristotle agrees that virtue cannot be learned from a book or a lecture: it requires embodied practice in order to learn how to deal with the feelings and thoughts that arise when we put ourselves, for a good reason, into a risky situation.

However, in my experience as a teacher, I find that many students are fearful of speaking their mind in class, wary of the judgment of their peers or professors. This is an important reason to seek discussion and broad participation in the classroom because it gives students an opportunity to practice speaking up and facing others respectfully while taking a stand for some idea or position or asking difficult questions that are vital to our growth as individuals and communities. We may think of this as the cultivation of intellectual courage rather than heroic moral courage, but since the respectful pursuit of truth is itself a noble goal, even the cultivation of intellectual courage has a moral dimension. Learning to lead an "examined life" like Socrates, thus, may help prepare us for more difficult moral challenges. Socrates's case stands as an enduring reminder that a commitment to intellectual courage may itself sometimes need to be defended with moral courage.

---

[14] Debra R. Comer and Michael Schwartz, "Highlighting Moral Courage in the Business Ethics Course," *Journal of Business Ethics* 146 (2017): 703–723.

[15] See Eric M. Peterson, "From Intellectual to Moral Courage," *Business Ethics Journal Review* 6:5 (2018), 24–29.

Summary

The readings in this unit offer an ethical frame of reference for thinking about the stressors that arise in practice and the vulnerabilities physical therapists face. Moral distress, burnout, and moral injury are complex issues in healthcare. Understood in ethical terms, these phenomena illuminate how institutional and noninstitutional factors affect clinicians' practice, performance, duties, and integrity.

Recall Gail's predicament. If Gail chooses to follow her professional duties and her oath to act in her patients' best interests, she may lose her job because she will not be able to meet productivity requirements. Without a salary, Gail would jeopardize her financial security and possibly default on her student loan. On the other hand, if Gail meets the requirements established by her employer, she may fail to satisfy her obligation to provide quality patient care. In return for maximizing productivity, she may feel dread and emotionally distressed over subpar work. Gail has limited options, and either choice will have considerable drawbacks. In this case, Gail is subject to competing obligations—namely, institutional, administrative, professional, and personal. Gail's choice will inevitably result in failing in at least one area of obligation. Gail may feel as if she is in an impossible situation, forced to choose between her values and the demands of her employer.

The pressures that jeopardize our moral values threaten our moral integrity. When we cannot fulfill our moral obligations, cracks form in our identity. We become morally compromised, like a building with a cracked foundation, susceptible to larger problems. Over time, our weakened moral self may encounter ethical flaws and failings.

If you are confronted with a situation that threatens your values and moral beliefs, be rational rather than impulsive. Upholding the ethical standards of your profession is essential to maintaining the public's trust. Upholding your personal values is essential to sleeping at night free of a guilty conscience. Work to find a balance, and if you cannot, communicate in a way that maintains respect among all parties and manifests your integrity. Courage requires you to take appropriate risks, not foolhardy leaps that result in self-sacrifice. Moral integrity in action is fueled by the virtue of courage. It enables us to be thoughtful about when—and if—to take action.

Sometimes choosing to be ethical is easy, but at other times, the available choices involve great sacrifice and risk. Work to cultivate habits that form a strong foundation for ethical practice. Moral integrity is nurtured over time, and good judgment requires training. Apply your values and virtues to action and take responsibility for your conduct.

The occurrence of moral distress, burnout, and moral injury cannot be resolved by individuals on their own. We must work together. Healthcare organizations have an obligation to promote a culture of wellness and compassion. Employees must be supported so that they can fulfill their oaths to their patients and satisfy their duties to the profession. We must remember that we all share the same goals in life—namely, to be happy, to live well, and to experience joy.

Comprehension Questions

Campbell, Ulrich, and Grady, *A Broader Understanding of Moral Distress*

1. According to the authors, what does the traditional characterization of moral distress lack?
2. Why is a broader understanding of moral distress important for clinicians?
3. In your own words, explain how uncertainty and guilt by association can lead to distress.
4. How does bad luck or bad outcomes affect one's integrity and moral sense of self?

Manning and Stroud, *Communicating with Integrity*

1. What are some of the good things we can do with communication?
2. What are some of the bad things we can do with communication?
3. How does communication orient us toward the world?
   a. What is persuasion-centered orientation?
   b. What is invitational orientation?
4. The authors specify two basic ethical standards for communication. In your own words, explain these standards and their importance to integrity.
5. Describe some of the central features of effective communication.

Pianalto, *Moral Courage*

1. Describe the similarities and differences between physical courage and moral courage.
2. What reasons does Pianalto offer for his claim that courage is a complex virtue?
3. What is the difference between thin and thick accounts of courage? Can a morally courageous person can act immorally?
4. What made Socrates refusal to leave Athens an act of courage?
5. What did Martin Luther King, Jr. say about the morality of Socrates' actions?

Gail's Story

Developing Your Moral Imagination: Critical Thinking Questions

1. Much recent work on clinical distress and burnout claim they are ethical issues. Do you agree with this position? Why, or why not? What do you see as some of the most morally troubling aspects of clinical distress and burnout?

2. Do you think good communication is a path for responding to stressors that impact the ability to make good choices? Is good communication one aspect of moral integrity?
3. Why is the cultivation of moral courage important for clinicians?
4. How do clinical distress and burnout affect the core values of accountability, duty, and integrity?
5. Reflect on what you have learned in this unit and reexamine Gail's situation. What should Gail do?

UNIT IV

Acting with Integrity in the Face of Uncertainty

··

Beth's Story

Beth is a neurologic certified specialist who works with poststroke individuals. Currently, Beth is caring for Vicki, an elderly patient who recently had a stroke. Vicki's neurological exam reveals severe damage; she is experiencing hemiparesis and is unable to live independently. Beth is uncertain of Vicki's condition. Beth does not know whether Vicki's paralysis is permanent, because her patient is suffering from a form of anosognosia, the denial of one's paralysis. Anosognosia is a neurological impairment involving perceptual deficits and is indicative of a poorer prognosis. Due to this complex neurological problem in which a patient denies their disease, Beth questions Vicki's ability to progress and improve function. Beth has been treating Vicki for four months poststroke, and her patient's progress appears to be plateauing. Beth is uncertain of how to proceed since her plan of care requires Vicki to understand the nature of her disabilities.

Schema Activation/Response Question

How can Beth best help Vicki?

Cultivating Professional Values

The APTA core values aim to promote good reasoning. The key values at stake in Beth's story include:

- **Accountability:** taking responsibility for one's actions and choices
- **Altruism:** sacrificing for others and putting others' needs before your own

- **Collaboration:** working together in pursuit of a shared goal
- **Compassion/Caring:** having kindness and finding importance in the suffering of others
- **Excellence:** possessing knowledge and skill and acquiring habits of lifelong learning
- **Integrity:** acting in accord with one's personal and professional moral identity

Introduction to the Topic

We live in an uncertain world and making decisions without complete knowledge is a part of life. In healthcare, providers who are confronted with uncertainty contend with a unique set of challenges. Clinicians have fiduciary obligations to their patients, and patients see their providers as experts with all the answers even when it is not always true. When the evidence does not support a clear diagnosis or plan of care because of unknown factors, providers often struggle to communicate with their patients. This unit looks at the meaning of uncertainty and offers practical guidance for developing habits conducive to ethical practice even when clinicians do not know the entire truth.

Introduction to the Readings

Uncertainty, Ignorance, and the Virtue of Humility

The first reading is a selection from *Apology*, a dialogue written by the ancient Greek philosopher Plato. *Apology* recounts Socrates's speech to a jury when he is on trial for his life. Socrates, Plato's main character in the dialogue, appeals to his audience about the importance of recognizing one's own ignorance. Plato's goal is to help people realize their lack of knowledge and see the error of their ways, especially when they act without full knowledge.

In the dialogue, Socrates learns that the gods profess that he is the wisest person. Socrates questions their claim and begins a quest to understand if the revelation is accurate. On this journey, he meets with reputedly wise individuals—namely, politicians, poets, and craftsmen. The politicians, Socrates discovers, possess reputation and social status, but they are for the most part ignorant, deceitful, and foolish. The poets, Socrates says, "not by wisdom do poets write poetry, but by a sort of genius and inspiration; they are like diviners or soothsayers who also say many fine things, but do not understand the meaning of them." As for the craftsmen, Socrates discovers that "even the good artisans fell into the same error as the poets;—because they were good workmen they thought that they also knew all sorts of high matters, and this defect in them overshadowed their wisdom." Socrates concludes that in spite of everything he learned, in spite of being able to recognize his ignorance, "that I was better off to be as I was."

Socrates articulates how genuine wisdom requires the recognition of ignorance. Wisdom requires humility. To illustrate what he means by "humility," Socrates recounts his confrontation with a man who professed himself to be wise. As he converses with the man, Socrates realizes that he knows that he does not know but the man fails to recognize that he does not know. Socrates states, "So I left him, saying to myself, as I went away: Well, although I do not suppose that either of us knows anything really beautiful and good, I am better off than he is,—for he knows nothing, and thinks that he knows; I neither know nor think that I know. In this latter particular, then, I seem to have slightly the advantage of him." Socrates comprehends his ignorance: he knows that he does not know. This story illuminates the classic philosophical problem known as the Socratic Paradox. We must first be able to recognize our uncertainty, ignorance, and doubt in order to have knowledge. Self-knowledge is the foundation for true understanding and awareness; it is the first step in the cultivation of humility.

In the second reading, "Epistemic Humility," authors David Dwight, Terry Grapentine, and David Soorholtz discuss a "stance that is appropriate to, and that acknowledges, our situation as fallible, limited beings that are prone to overconfidence and error." The text describes both the practical nature of epistemic humility and the importance of cultivating this virtue to make good judgments. The authors present an example of humility by telling the Greek story of Odysseus and the Sirens. Odysseus recognized and accepted his limits; he was not overconfident in his ability to resist the Sirens' songs.

The authors describe how both confirmation bias and overconfidence can impair our judgments. These cognitive strategies predispose us and impact the way we collect and assess information. Confirmation bias affects how we collect and interpret information to support our beliefs. Overconfidence is a cognitive habit that involves overestimating our abilities and talents. The authors encourage readers to become more aware of their epistemic position—namely, the beliefs we hold and the information environment in which we are enmeshed. Both our beliefs and biases can dramatically influence our judgments and corresponding behaviors. Thus, we must acknowledge poor cognitive habits, and we must work to minimize their influence on our conduct. The authors state: "By accepting and even embracing our limitations and failings as cognitive agents, rather than denying them or struggling against them, it's possible to improve the quality of our judgments and make more rational decisions than we would otherwise." The cultivation of epistemic humility is one strategy that enables good judgment and good actions.

Uncertainty in Healthcare

Sometimes we lack all the facts, and sometimes we cannot interpret the facts. Yet we want to do the best we can. The previous readings demonstrate that to cultivate good character we must strive for self-knowledge and overcome cognitive bias. Ethics involves making decisions that affect others, and ethics can be especially challenging when we make decisions under uncertainty. In healthcare decisions, the stakes are especially high because our choices affect patients' lives.

I wrote the final reading, "Uncertainty in Healthcare: Clinical and Philosophical Perspectives," to examine the nature of uncertainty. By drawing on insights from French philosopher René Descartes, I offer a philosophical analysis of uncertainty. I examine the practical consequences of uncertainty in healthcare practice and recommend empathy as a possible strategy for abating its effects. By helping clinicians recognize the forms of uncertainty, they can respond more effectively and avoid the harms that arise when we ignore what we do not know.

Indeed, ignorance and doubt limit our ability to respond and function in the world. Healthcare providers can learn to cultivate dispositions and cognitive behaviors adept at detecting the limits that define their practice. Providers can, for example, learn to model integrity and collaborate with others. When clinicians know their limits in the face of uncertainty, they can make good judgments, judgments that align with their moral obligations.

References

Beresford, Eric B. "Uncertainty and the Shaping of Medical Decisions." *Hastings Center Report* 21, no. 4 (1991): 6–11.

Eddy, David M. "Variations in Physical Practice: The Role of Uncertainty." *Health Affairs* 3 (1984): 74–89.

Fox, Renée C. "The Evolution of Medical Uncertainty." *Milbank Memorial Fund Quarterly/Health and Society* 58, no. 1 (1980): 1–49.

Hahn, Paul K. J., William M. P. Klein, and Neeraj K. Arora. "Varieties of Uncertainty in Health Care: A Conceptual Taxonomy." *Medical Decision Making* 31, no. 6 (2011): 828–838.

Pomare, Chiara, Kate Churruca, Louise A. Ellis, Janet C. Long, and Jeffrey Braithwaite. "A revised model of uncertainty in complex healthcare settings: A scoping review." *Journal of Evaluative Clinical Practice* 25 (2019): 176–182.

Selection from "Apology"

By Plato

Now I regard this as a fair challenge, and I will endeavour to explain to you the reason why I am called wise and have such an evil fame. Please to attend then. And although some of you may think that I am joking, I declare that I will tell you the entire truth. Men of Athens, this reputation of mine has come of a certain sort of wisdom which I possess. If you ask me what kind of wisdom, I reply, wisdom such as may perhaps be attained by man, for to that extent I am inclined to believe that I am wise; whereas the persons of whom I was speaking have a superhuman wisdom which I may fail to describe, because I have it not myself; and he who says that I have, speaks falsely, and is taking away my character. And here, O men of Athens, I must beg you not to interrupt me, even if I seem to say something extravagant. For the word which I will speak is not mine. I will refer you to a witness who is worthy of credit; that witness shall be the God of Delphi—he will tell you about my wisdom, if I have any, and of what sort it is. You must have known Chaerephon; he was early a friend of mine, and also a friend of yours, for he shared in the recent exile of the people, and returned with you. Well, Chaerephon, as you know, was very impetuous in all his doings, and he went to Delphi and boldly asked the oracle to tell him whether—as I was saying, I must beg you not to interrupt—he asked the oracle to tell him whether anyone was wiser than I was, and the Pythian prophetess answered, that there was no man wiser. Chaerephon is dead himself; but his brother, who is in court, will confirm the truth of what I am saying.

Why do I mention this? Because I am going to explain to you why I have such an evil name. When I heard the answer, I said to myself, What can the god mean? and what is the interpretation of his riddle? for I know that I have no wisdom, small or great. What then can he mean when he says that I am the wisest of men? And yet he is a god, and cannot lie; that would be against his nature. After long consideration, I thought of a method of trying the question. I reflected that if I could only find a man wiser than myself, then I might go to the god with a refutation in my hand. I should say to him, "Here is a man who is wiser than I am; but you said that I was the wisest." Accordingly I

Plato, Selection from "Apology," trans. Benjamin Jowett, 1871.

went to one who had the reputation of wisdom, and observed him—his name I need not mention; he was a politician whom I selected for examination—and the result was as follows: When I began to talk with him, I could not help thinking that he was not really wise, although he was thought wise by many, and still wiser by himself; and thereupon I tried to explain to him that he thought himself wise, but was not really wise; and the consequence was that he hated me, and his enmity was shared by several who were present and heard me. So I left him, saying to myself, as I went away: Well, although I do not suppose that either of us knows anything really beautiful and good, I am better off than he is,—for he knows nothing, and thinks that he knows; I neither know nor think that I know. In this latter particular, then, I seem to have slightly the advantage of him. Then I went to another who had still higher pretensions to wisdom, and my conclusion was exactly the same. Whereupon I made another enemy of him, and of many others besides him.

Then I went to one man after another, being not unconscious of the enmity which I provoked, and I lamented and feared this: but necessity was laid upon me,—the word of God, I thought, ought to be considered first. And I said to myself, Go I must to all who appear to know, and find out the meaning of the oracle. And I swear to you, Athenians, by the dog I swear!—for I must tell you the truth—the result of my mission was just this: I found that the men most in repute were all but the most foolish; and that others less esteemed were really wiser and better. I will tell you the tale of my wanderings and of the "Herculean" labours, as I may call them, which I endured only to find at last the oracle irrefutable. After the politicians, I went to the poets; tragic, dithyrambic, and all sorts. And there, I said to myself, you will be instantly detected; now you will find out that you are more ignorant than they are. Accordingly, I took them some of the most elaborate passages in their own writings, and asked what was the meaning of them—thinking that they would teach me something. Will you believe me? I am almost ashamed to confess the truth, but I must say that there is hardly a person present who would not have talked better about their poetry than they did themselves. Then I knew that not by wisdom do poets write poetry, but by a sort of genius and inspiration; they are like diviners or soothsayers who also say many fine things, but do not understand the meaning of them. The poets appeared to me to be much in the same case; and I further observed that upon the strength of their poetry they believed themselves to be the wisest of men in other things in which they were not wise. So I departed, conceiving myself to be superior to them for the same reason that I was superior to the politicians.

At last I went to the artisans. I was conscious that I knew nothing at all, as I may say, and I was sure that they knew many fine things; and here I was not mistaken, for they did know many things of which I was ignorant, and in this they certainly were wiser than I was. But I observed that even the good artisans fell into the same error as the poets;—because they were good workmen they thought that they also knew all sorts of high matters, and this defect in them overshadowed their wisdom; and therefore I asked myself on behalf of the oracle, whether I would like to be as I was, neither having their knowledge nor their ignorance, or like them in both; and I made answer to myself and to the oracle that I was better off as I was.

Epistemic Humility

By David Dwight, Terry Grapentine, and David Soorholtz

If we know that we're prone to confirmation bias, but that this bias can be neutralized by following certain scientific protocols, or by reasoning together in diverse groups, then this can lead to strategies for effectively managing and reducing the effects of this bias.

Also, if we know that we're prone to confirmation bias, and we know that we're also prone to overconfidence, then it helps us to identify certain attitudes, or virtues, that should be cultivated to help avoid the effects of these biases.

One of these attitudes is what I like to call epistemic humility. "Epistemic" is a philosopher's term that means "pertaining to knowledge," so in this respect I'm talking about humility regarding the status of our knowledge and our capacity to reason well.

Now, this isn't the same as skepticism about *knowledge*—to be epistemically humble isn't necessarily to *doubt* our knowledge, or to deny the possibility of knowledge. It's rather to adopt an epistemic stance that is appropriate to, and that acknowledges, our situation as fallible, limited beings that are prone to overconfidence and error.

The degree to which we're prone to error will vary from context to context. The key idea here is that the quality of our judgments is highest when our epistemic stance—the attitude we take toward our own status and capacities as knowers—properly matches the epistemic environment in which we find ourselves. For example, if we're reasoning all by ourselves, this is a different epistemic environment than if we're reasoning with a diverse group of people. Given what we know about reasoning, it's appropriate to adopt a greater degree of epistemic humility when we're reasoning by ourselves than when we're reasoning with a diverse group.

And sometimes the appropriate stance is simply to not trust our own judgments at all. That's an extreme form of humility, but in the right circumstances it can be the most rational stance to take.

A classic example of this kind of rational humility can be found in the Greek story of Odysseus and the Sirens. The Sirens were these mythic female creatures who sang these beautiful songs that lured sailors into the water ... (crashing) their boats onto the shores of their island.

Odysseus was very curious to know what the Siren song sounded like, but he understood that he may not be able to resist their song. So he did something very clever; he had all his sailors plug their ears with beeswax and tie him to the mast. He ordered his men to leave him tied tightly to the mast, no matter how much he might beg to untie him.

When he heard the Sirens' beautiful song he was overcome by it and he desperately wanted to jump into the sea to join them, and as he predicted he ordered the sailors to untie him. But they refused based on his earlier orders. So, *as a result of his strong sense of rational humility regarding his own capacity to resist persuasion, Odysseus was able to experience the Sirens' song and come out unscathed, where other men with less humility were lured to their deaths.*

For critical thinkers the moral of this parable is clear. Although it may seem counterintuitive, by accepting and even embracing our limitations and failings as cognitive agents, rather than denying them or struggling against them, it's possible to improve the quality of our judgments and make more rational decisions than we would otherwise. But to pull this off we need to cultivate the right kind of epistemic virtues that are informed by the right kind of background knowledge, and through knowledge and experience, learn to develop the appropriate judgment about the right level of epistemic humility to adopt in any particular circumstance.

From a marketer's point of view, there is a practical problem associated with being epistemically humble— time! Events and circumstances often conspire to take away available time to ponder and research our arguments. There never seems to be enough of it to make good decisions; although marketers are forced to find time to fix the bad ones.

An example of this was when Fresh Market, a specialty grocery chain, rushed the decision to open a store in Des Moines, Iowa, in October 2015, only to close it seven months later.[1] Although we're speculating somewhat, Fresh Market did not seem to have grasped the level of competition in this market for fresh fruits and vegetables from Hy-Vee, a regional grocery store chain, or the other already established specialty grocery stores, Trader Joe's and Whole Foods. Statements about Fresh Market's future competition would have formed part of the premises of their argument to open a Des Moines store.

At the heart of Fresh Market's decision to open their Iowa location lies the remnants of a collection of poor premises—known only to its senior executives—supporting their argument's weak and likely uncogent conclusion: "Therefore, we should open a store in Des Moines, Iowa."

Takeaways

- *Epistemic humility* is being "mindful of our innate reasoning shortcomings and striving to make fewer reasoning errors by using good, truth-conducive reasoning tools."[2]
- Epistemic humility does not mean that we are skeptical of our ability to generate *knowledge*—justified, true-beliefs. It just means that we are humble about our ability to do so.
- A major obstacle that confronts our ability to act with epistemic humility is *time*. The pressures of the day-to-day business world and the various demands on our schedules conspire to force us not to take the time required, or invest the resources needed, to construct good arguments. Therefore, we too often find ourselves falling back on unreliable decision-making heuristics and undependable gut reactions to solve marketing problems.
- It seems that there is never enough time to make sound and cogent arguments; yet we are forced to make time to clean up our mistakes. Find the logic in that!

Uncertainty in Healthcare

Clinical and Philosophical Perspectives

By Katherine K. Johnson

Introduction

Uncertainty is an ever-present and often unacknowledged obstacle in healthcare. A lack of knowledge, ambiguous information, unpredictable outcomes, and incomplete evidence can limit providers' abilities to function proficiently. Most accounts of uncertainty argue that it is a barrier to knowledge acquisition and stress its negative qualities. We want to avoid a state of doubt because it often has a destabilizing effect on our ability to make responsible decisions.

Situations of uncertainty are indeed disruptive; however, they can provide us the opportunity to be innovative. As biologist Stuart Firestein argues, ignorance provides the fuel for the pursuit of truth and the desire to learn and understand.[1] Firestein stresses that even though vast quantities of knowledge have been discovered in the world, we will likely never know it all. Doubt and inhabiting a state of not knowing provide an opening to consider obstacles in a different way.

Despite scientific and medical advances, uncertainty endures. Healthcare workers must learn to live with it because it is irremediable; we will never know everything. However, if healthcare providers have a better understanding of the reach of uncertainty, they can more efficiently maneuver around its challenges.

This [reading] explores the presence and influence of uncertainty in healthcare. I present various perspectives of uncertainty and highlight their crucial features. I illuminate the connection between ethics and the diverse manifestations of uncertainty in the healthcare environment. By learning to identify the invisible presence and sources of uncertainty, healthcare providers can improve their response to it and prevent potential harms.

---

[1] Stuart Firestein, *Ignorance: How It Drives Science* (New York: Oxford University Press, 2012).

Philosophical Perspectives on Uncertainty

Philosophers have been preoccupied with investigating knowledge since antiquity. Epistemology, the study of knowledge, seeks to understand the nature of knowledge—its sources and its value. While numerous philosophers argue that we can possess genuine knowledge, some theorists, known as skeptics, dispute the possibility of knowledge. These skeptics contend that we can never be certain of anything. From a philosophical point of view, uncertainty is crucial to an understanding of knowledge. In philosophy, uncertainty is generally characterized as a form of not knowing and a species of ignorance. Uncertainty involves an attitude of doubt, a lack of confidence in one's beliefs, and a hesitancy about the truth value of facts.

Sixteenth century French philosopher René Descartes plays a historically crucial role in the search for knowledge. In his classic work *Meditations on First Philosophy*, Descartes argues that all knowledge claims must be indubitable—namely, beyond all doubt.[2] For Descartes, uncertainty involves the presence of doubt.

In his quest for certainty, Descartes employs his "method of doubt," a process of deliberate, rational thinking. Utilizing this methodology, Descartes shows us that the veracity of many of our long-standing beliefs about ourselves and the world are suspect. Descartes presents the reader with a hypothetical thought experiment aimed at undermining some of our most ordinary beliefs. He imagines that we may be subject to a deception orchestrated by an evil genius and that everything we once believed to be true may, in fact, be false:

> Accordingly, I will suppose not a supremely good God, the source of truth, but rather an evil genius, supremely powerful and clever, who has directed his entire effort at deceiving me. I will regard the heavens, the air, the earth, colors, shapes, sounds, and all external things as nothing but the bedeviling hoaxes of my dreams, with which he lays snares for my credulity. I will regard myself as not having hands, or eyes, or flesh, or blood, or any senses, but as nevertheless falsely believing that I possess all these things.[3]

In his imagining, the evil genius's duplicity is so complete that Descartes is unable to recognize both truth and falsity. Even long-held beliefs, such as the belief that he has a body, is suspicious. The point of Descartes's evil genius hypothesis is simple: If I cannot rule out the possibility that I am being systematically deceived by an evil genius, then I cannot know what I think I know. Further, since I cannot rule out this possibility, I cannot be certain of anything. Therefore, I must live in uncertainty.

---

[2] René Descartes, *Meditations on First Philosophy*, 3rd ed., trans. Donald A. Cress (Indianapolis, IN: Hackett Publishing Company, 1993).

[3] Descartes, *Meditations*, 16–17.

Descartes teaches us to question the reliability of the foundations of our beliefs. He encourages us to ask why we believe what we do and whether we have a good basis for our beliefs. Answering these questions enables us to be critically reflective. This critical skill involves observation, awareness, and insight. Moreover, asking these questions helps facilitate our responsibility for the content of our beliefs.

Uncertainty can arise from various causes, ranging from cognitive constraints, to unpredictability, to instances of chance that block access to evidence. Uncertainty can result from unintended influences of which we are often unaware. Further, uncertainty can be the result of poor or immature cognitive mechanisms, such as cognitive dissonance or overconfidence. Indeed, uncertainty reveals our insecurities about the reliability and truth of information, evidence, and our beliefs.

Uncertainty has both theoretical and practical dimensions. Theoretically, uncertainty describes the epistemic state of an agent who lacks either evidence or a method crucial to prove truth. Uncertainty also defines a position of skepticism in which we are unable to state that we know anything indubitably. Practically, uncertainty impairs our ability to act and to make good judgments. When we lack information, we are at risk of making mistakes and causing harm. The ability to recognize uncertain—and doubtful—beliefs is crucial for minimizing the possibility of error.

When we lack conviction about the truth of our beliefs, we may also lack confidence in our judgments. Uncertainty has serious practical implications because it is an imbedded feature of decision-making. Most decision-making frameworks articulate the steps involved in making good judgments. However, these structures are based on three apparent assumptions: first, that we can gather all the facts; second, that we can correctly evaluate the information; and third, that we can apply our understanding of the facts to the relevant features and goals of the situation.

Sometimes, however, we lack all the facts, we overestimate or underestimate the meaning of evidence, and we cannot foresee the future trajectory of our proposed actions. Clearly, these inadequacies affect our capacity to make judgments with confidence and to achieve our goals. Moreover, these defects can impair our ability to fulfill our moral duties and obligations. Uncertainty encompasses not only a lack of knowledge about nonmoral matters of fact but also a lack of understanding of the moral facts, including our moral duties and obligations.

Empathy and the Ethical Significance of Uncertainty

Doing the right thing requires choosing the right thing, but first we must know what the right thing is. Often, we cannot know the right course of action, because uncertainty clouds our capacity to make clear and proficient judgments.

Moral confusion is a serious consequence of uncertainty. Imagine a clinician faced with recommending a treatment with uncertain benefits. The provider struggles to articulate ambiguous information and fears their patient may refuse treatment. As a result, they experience moral confusion and distress because they are unable to effectively communicate with their patient. They feel as if they are compromising their values and may distance themselves from their patient. In a situation like this, a clinician may struggle to act in a way that aligns with their professional and ethical commitments because uncertainty obscures their ability to see opportunities for improvement.

The cultivation of empathy is one possible strategy for abating the effects of uncertainty. Despite less-than-perfect knowledge, clinicians can build empathy. Empathy is a capacity that involves an appreciation of another's suffering; it prompts an active desire to help and promote the good.[4] A disposition of empathy can work together with altruism, an attitude of selflessness and care for the well-being of others.[5] Empathy is a motivator; it can improve how we help others, such as the way that we care for them.[6] Cultivating empathy can promote a deeper connection in the shared activity of decision-making and can support honest, clear communication. A clinician who recognizes and values their patient's suffering is better equipped to express confusing and unclear information in a way that is compassionate and caring.

Empathy has many moral uses. It motivates us to do good, to build and sustain relationships, and to make moral judgments.[7] When we are motivated to do good, we look for opportunities to help. When we appreciate the suffering of others, we can better connect with and understand their needs. When we care about others, we are more deliberate and cautious. If we take steps to improve our epistemic position, we can allay potential harms that might arise from uncertainty.

Healthcare workers can learn to cultivate dispositions and behaviors attuned to diagnosing the limits that define their practice. Sometimes we are neither clinically nor ethically prepared to respond in an ambiguous situation. Unpreparedness can result in both poor outcomes and ethical compromise. Clinicians can avoid subjecting patients to unnecessary risk if clear standards are articulated. Priorities must be established. Expectations must be communicated. Values must be expressed. When providers recognize their limits, they can make good judgments that align with their professional standards of care, moral obligations, and duties to patients. Healthcare workers must ascertain the presence of uncertainty and act proactively.

Articulating Uncertainty in Clinical Practice

Decision-making is a constant activity in healthcare practice, and providers need information to make decisions. However, the healthcare environment is undoubtedly clouded by uncertainty. As a pervasive fixture, uncertainty affects clinicians' abilities to make decisions, to benefit patients, and to collaborate with other professionals. Providers need firm foundations for having confidence in

---

[4] J. D. Trout, *Why Empathy Matters: The Science and Psychology of Better Judgment* (New York: Penguin Books, 2009).

[5] Michael Slote, *The Ethics of Care and Empathy* (London: Routledge, 2007).

[6] The benefit of empathy is exemplified in various formulations of an ethics of care. For example, see Michael Slote, *The Ethics of Care and Empathy* and Nel Noddings, *Caring: A Relational Approach to Ethics and Moral Education* (Berkeley, CA: University of California Press, 1986).

[7] Hannah Read, "A Typology of Empathy and Its Many Moral Forms," *Philosophy Compass* 14, no. 10 (2019): 5–7.

their beliefs, especially when those beliefs influence choice and action. Learning the nature, extent, and forms of uncertainty can help clinicians in many ways, especially in interactions with patients, families, and other professionals.

Uncertainty in healthcare can undermine reliable, safe, and quality care. Further, uncertainty about the most moral course of action may create distress. Imagine a clinician who is unable to diagnosis a patient due to incomplete information. As a result, they are unable to recommend treatment because they doubt the precise nature of their patient's ailment. The provider is unable to make a decision and communicate effectively with their patient. Problematic situations like this are common in healthcare and cause providers distress, confusion, and anxiety. However, providers must learn to understand uncertainty so that they can convey it to patients.

The challenge of articulating uncertainty is a hurdle that takes time, a scarce resource for practitioners. Time constraints and complexity further exacerbate clinicians' preparedness to confront both clinical and ethical conflicts. Bad judgments and poor outcomes may result, and clinicians may fail to fulfill their fiduciary, professional, and moral obligations.

Medical literature describes uncertainty, in the most general terms, as a lack of knowledge and understanding. In 1957, sociologist Renée Fox refined this understanding, presenting the first comprehensive account categorizing uncertainty in medicine.[8] Her classification system lists three dimensions of uncertainty. The first category focuses on the provider's knowledge base and skill set, what Fox describes as the "incomplete or imperfect mastery of available knowledge."[9] The second category concentrates more broadly on the boundaries of knowledge in the medical field and the "limitations in current medical knowledge."[10] The third category of uncertainty involves a combination of the preceding elements, specifically the "difficulty of distinguishing between personal ignorance or ineptitude and the limitations of present medical knowledge."[11]

Since Fox's initial contribution, various scholars highlight features outside of Fox's initial focus on medical knowledge and skill. They stress the destabilizing effect of uncertainty on both clinical decision-making and providers' ethical commitments.[12] Contemporary taxonomies attempt to account for the multifaceted occurrences of uncertainty in complex healthcare environments. These classificatory systems provide a broader perspective of the scope, influence, and risks associated with doubt in clinical settings.

For example, one of the most inclusive formulations of uncertainty incorporates a three-dimensional taxonomy. In this model, the three fundamental classifications of uncertainty in healthcare include

---

[8] Renée Fox, "Training for Uncertainty," in *The Student-Physician: Introduction Studies in the Sociology of Medical Education*, ed. R. Merton, G. C. Reader, and P. Kendall (Cambridge, MA: Harvard University Press, 1957), 207–241; Renée Fox, "The Evolution of Medical Uncertainty," *Milbank Memorial Fund Quarterly/Health and Society* 58, no. 1 (1980): 1–49.

[9] Fox, "Training for Uncertainty," 208–209.

[10] Fox, "Training for Uncertainty," 208–209.

[11] Fox, "Training for Uncertainty", 208–209.

[12] Eric B. Beresford, "Uncertainty and the Shaping of Medical Decisions," *Hastings Center Report* 21, no. 4 (1991): 6–11.

the scientific (data centered), the practical (system centered), and the personal (patient centered).[13] The scientific domain includes uncertainty surrounding diagnosis, prognosis, causal explanations of disease and illness, and the efficacy of treatment recommendations. For example, clinicians may confront diagnostic uncertainty when incomplete or ambiguous information reveals inconclusive results about the cause of a patient's illness. The practical dimension involves uncertainty about the structure of care, the processes of care, and the complexity of health systems. Providers, for example, may struggle to negotiate organizational demands and confront situations when general policies fail to provide clear guidance in context-specific situations.[14] The personal aspect encompasses psychosocial features, existential aspects, and ethical considerations.[15] For example, when an incompetent patient is unable to express their wishes, a provider may doubt the course of action that matches their ethical commitments.[16] These areas often overlap and comingle, generating even more complex situations of uncertainty. This integrated model catalogs a robust spectrum of uncertainty across these three distinct yet interrelated realms and is applicable across various healthcare systems and environments.[17]

Taxonomies of uncertainty are a useful resource for clinicians' daily practice. These classification systems provide a roadmap for clinicians to be critically reflective. By learning to observe and identify uncertainty, providers can rise above obstacles that inhibit effective practice. Clinicians must learn to recognize the multiform manifestations of uncertainty in order to mitigate the dangers that occur when they ignore or underappreciate what they do not know. Overlooking the limits of knowledge is negligence, a violation of a basic standard of due care. Providers have a fundamental moral duty to both promote the good and minimize the risk of harm.

Uncertainty shapes healthcare practice in both negative and positive ways. Negatively, uncertainty is manipulative, deceiving providers and weaving false narratives of certainty. In response, clinicians must become adaptive; they must accept the actuality of uncertainty and treat it as a fixed feature of the clinical experience.[18] Positively, uncertainty can be useful to clinicians, offering opportunities for innovative thinking. With this attitude, clinicians can meditate situations of doubt, promote mutual good will, and prevent unintentional violations of trust.

---

[13] Paul K. J. Han, William M. P. Klein, and Neeraj K. Aurora, "Varieties of Uncertainty in Healthcare: A Conceptual Taxonomy," *Medical Decision Making* 31, no. 6 (2011): 828–838; Chiara Pomare et al., "A Revised Model of Uncertainty in Complex Health-care Settings: A Scoping Review," *Journal of Evaluation in Clinical Practice* 25 (2019): 176–182.

[14] Pomare et al., "Revised Model of Uncertainty," 178, 180–181.

[15] Pomare et al. build upon Han et al.'s model and introduce systems uncertainty and ethical uncertainty. Systems uncertainty acknowledges the lack of clarity in organizational policies and systems guidelines. Ethical uncertainty refers to moral inconsistencies among professionals, employers, and society. See Pomare et al., "Revised Model of Uncertainty," 178, Table 1, 180.

[16] Beresford, "Uncertainty and Shaping," 7.

[17] Pomare et al., "Revised Model of Uncertainty," 180–181.

[18] See Fox, "Evolution of Medical Uncertainty"; Beresford, "Uncertainty and Shaping"; and Jonathan Koffman et al., "Uncertainty and COVID-19: How are We to Respond?" *The Royal Society of Medicine* 113, no. 6 (2020): 211–216.

Conclusion

While healthcare providers are not flawless, they ought to strive to be faultless. Clinicians cannot always avoid the pitfalls and harms that arise from uncertainty. However, they can still make good judgments despite ambiguity. People tend to praise or condemn judgments based on outcomes. However, unpredictability makes absolute certainty impossible. Rather than basing judgments solely on outcomes, clinicians also ought to be evaluated on *how* they made their decision.[19] Failure to proactively recognize and calculate the unknowns of a situation is a moral dereliction. Providers must have confidence in their decisions, which necessitates that they assess their fallibility. Clinicians must think about the reliability of the evidence along with the sources and structures that provide the information. Recall the lessons of Descartes: We must ask why we believe what we beleive and whether we have a good basis for our beliefs. We must utilize responsible and reflective belief-forming practices, such as the cultivation of epistemic humility, that enhance our epistemic position and minimize the harmful effects of doubt.

Ignorance, unpredictability, and doubt can also affect patients. Patients can be vulnerable, scared, and eager to understand their condition. Patients are often desperate to identify the causes of their illness or disability, and they want to find a cure. Patients' knowledge is inevitably limited, but the desire for an explanation often leads to a desperate search for answers. When the search for a cause is fruitless, patients often draw conclusions that are unsubstantiated by evidence. Unsupported beliefs can be dangerous, leading patients to make ineffective health decisions. In this climate, a clinician's duty to diagnose uncertainty becomes even more crucial.

Healthcare providers can mitigate the effects of uncertainty in order to respond to patient needs. By cultivating empathy and learning patient's values and beliefs, providers can effectively collaborate in spite of uncertainty. Indeed, the goals of healthcare demand that clinicians not only work in the best interests of patients but also alongside their patients.

References

Beresford, Eric B. "Uncertainty and the Shaping of Medical Decisions." *The Hastings Center Report* 21, no. 4 (1991): 6–11.

Coplan, Amy, and Peter Goldie, eds. *Empathy: Philosophical and Psychological Perspectives.* New York: Oxford University Press, 2011.

Descartes, René. *Meditations on First Philosophy.* 3rd ed. Translated by Donald A. Cress. Indianapolis, IN: Hackett Publishing Company, 1993.

---

[19] Daniel Kahneman defends the moral importance of the decision-making process and not merely the outcomes of one's choice in his book, *Thinking, Fast and Slow* (New York: Farrar, Strauss, and Giroux, 2011), 408–418.

Djulbegovic, Benjamin, Iztok Hozo, and Sander Greenland. "Uncertainty in Clinical Medicine." In *Handbook of the Philosophy of Science*. Vol. 16, *Philosophy of Medicine*, edited by Fred Gifford, 299–356. Oxford, UK: Elsevier, 2011.

Eddy, David M. "Variations in Physician Practice: The Role of Uncertainty." *Health Affairs* (Millwood) 3, no. 2 (1984): 74–89.

Firestein, Stuart. *Ignorance: How It Drives Science*. New York: Oxford University Press, 2012.

Fox, Renée C. "The Evolution of Medical Uncertainty." *Milbank Memorial Fund Quarterly/Health and Society* 58, no. 1 (1980): 1–49.

Fox, Renée C. "Training for Uncertainty." In *The Student-Physician: Introductory Studies in the Sociology of Medical Education*. Edited by Robert K. Merton, George G. Reader, and Patricia Kendall, 207–241. Cambridge, MA: Harvard University Press, 1957.

Gilligan, Carol. *In a Different Voice: Psychological Theory and Women's Development*. Cambridge, MA: Harvard University Press, 1982.

Han, Paul K. J., William M. P. Klein, and Neeraj K Arora. "Varieties of Uncertainty in Healthcare: A Conceptual Taxonomy." *Medical Decision Making* 31, no. 6 (2011): 828–838.

Kahneman, Daniel. *Thinking, Fast and Slow*. New York: Farrar, Strauss, and Giroux, 2011.

Katz, Leon. "Why Doctors Don't Disclose Uncertainty." *Hastings Center Report* 14, no. 1 (1984): 35–44.

Koffman, Jonathan, Jamie Gross, Simon Noah Etkind, and Lucy Selman. "Uncertainty and COVID-19: How Are We to Respond?" *The Royal Society of Medicine* 113, no. 6 (2020): 211–216.

Lockhart, Ted. *Moral Uncertainty and Its Consequences*. New York, Oxford University Press, 2000.

Noddings, Nel. *Caring: A Relational Approach to Morality and Moral Education*. Berkeley, CA: University of California Press, 1986.

Pomare, Chiara, Kate Churruca, Louise A. Ellis, Janet C. Long, and Jeffrey Braithwaite. "A Revised Model of Uncertainty in Complex Healthcare Settings: A Scoping Review." *Journal of Evaluation in Clinical Practice* 25 (2019): 176–182.

Read, Hannah. "A Typology of Empathy and Its Many Moral Forms." *Philosophy Compass* 14, no. 10 (2019): 1–12.

Slote, Michael. *The Ethics of Care and Empathy*. London: Routledge, 2007.

Trout, J. D. *Why Empathy Matters: The Science and Psychology of Better Judgment*. New York: Penguin Books, 2009.

Summary

Healthcare providers want to make the best choices possible. However, they inevitably have less-than-perfect information and limited time. Moreover, once a decision is made, they cannot go back in time for corrections. How do providers make informed decisions when they do not know the future? Situations that involve uncertainty, ignorance, or doubt are not ideal for effective decision-making. Think back to Beth's situation. Beth is accountable to her patient; she must fulfill both her fiduciary obligations and her commitment to honesty even though she lacks crucial information. She lacks important diagnostic information to identify manageable goals for Vicki's therapy. Vicki's cognitive impairment caused by the stroke further complicates the situation. Nevertheless, Beth must continue to maintain the bond of trust with Vicki. Clearly, a multiplicity of ethical considerations are at stake.

Clinicians can preserve patient trust by cultivating practices that respond to the unknown. Developing a disposition of epistemic humility is one way to combat uncertainty, doubt, and ignorance. Humility does not enable us to know the unknowns but understanding the situation and our limits can greatly help us avoid unethical behaviors and maintain professional duties. Understanding our limited knowledge is essential. Self-knowledge—namely, the recognition of one's ignorance—can empower clinicians to avoid ethical trade-offs that sacrifice their personal and professional values. Developing the moral imagination can help providers to be creative when faced with ethical conflict, uncertainty, and the barriers present in organizational cultures.

The cultivation of humility improves cooperation and maintains honesty. Humility is an aspect of character at the core of integrity. Humility motivates us to learn, helps us to recognize our ignorance and biases, and promotes good habits of thinking and judgment. Good habits help clinicians manage and respond to obstacles. Moreover, cultivating wholeness of character—namely, integrity—also promotes the integrity of the profession.

Ignorance is unavoidable, but its harmful consequences can be mitigated if we are careful and proactive. Clinicians must work to develop practices that enhance their ability to make decisions under uncertainty and without bias. Advocate for your patient's best interests in spite of skepticism.

Ethics is more than choosing and acting. Ethics also involves understanding. In fact, the first step toward making ethical choices is understanding the situation and context in which we are embedded. We often make moral decisions on our own, but sometimes we can do better if we gather feedback from others. The mentor–mentee relationship can provide perspective and help providers incorporate ethical behaviors that are empathetic, reflective, and deliberate.

Start by understanding the situation, the conflicts, and your obligations. Then be constructive in terms of action; recognize your limits and be proactive. Pragmatic thinking is prone to ethical compromise and backsliding, which can threaten your patients and breach your fiduciary obligations. For example, Beth thinks about proceeding with a plan of care that does not follow the standards of evidence-based practice. However, she realizes that she could jeopardize any future progress if she treats Vicki without adequate information about the severity of her neurological impairments. Beth would threaten the trust she has built with Vicki. Instead, Beth decides to consult with Vicki's neurologist and to gather information. She seeks advice from professionals familiar with the effects of anosognosia. Beth resolves to follow best practices of evidence-based care.

Healthcare providers cannot remove doubt and uncertainty. However, by remaining steadfast in pursuit of a shared goal with patients, clinicians can communicate uncertainty in a way that does not disentangle trust but rather promotes empathy and minimizes stress. Providers can maintain ethical standards and professional duties of care in spite of uncertainty.

Comprehension Questions

Plato, *Apology*

1. What does Socrates mean when he says, "When I do not know, neither do I think I know"?
2. Why does Socrates think that self-knowledge is important?
3. What does Socrates learn about the politicians, the poets, and the craftsmen?
4. According to Socrates, what does it mean to be wise?

Dwight, Grapentine, and Soorholtz, *Epistemic Humility*

1. How do the authors define "epistemic humility"?
2. What is the central lesson in the story of Odysseus and the Sirens?
3. What makes the cultivation of epistemic humility valuable to professionals?
4. Why should we learn to identify our epistemic limitations?

Johnson, *Understanding Uncertainty: Clinical and Philosophical Perspectives*

1. What does Descartes teach us about uncertainty?
2. What are the various divisions of uncertainty in clinical practice?
3. What are some examples of uncertainty in healthcare?
4. What is empathy, and why is it a useful strategy for responding to situations of uncertainty?

Beth's Story

Developing Your Moral Imagination: Critical Thinking Questions

1. Think back to a time when you were uncertain of a patient's diagnosis, recovery goals, or plan of care. What did you do? Looking back, what would you change?

2. Why is humility an important character trait for clinicians?

3. If you were Beth, how would you gather information about your patient?

4. When is pragmatic thinking valuable, and when should practical considerations be put aside?

5. What common features do philosophical and clinical accounts of uncertainty share?

UNIT V

Hope in the Patient Encounter

....

Steven's Story

Patients with incomplete spinal cord injuries often have unpredictable recoveries; the degree of their neurological and functional return may take years to determine. Picture Leon, a patient who recently suffered an incomplete spinal cord injury. He asks Steven, his physical therapist, if he will ever walk again. Steven feels conflicted. Steven knows that the damage to Leon's spinal cord is severe but also that the injury is not complete. His experience with other patients and the reports from the neurologist tell Steven the odds of a full recovery are slim. Steven must decide whether and how to inform Leon that he is unlikely to ever walk again. Steven is concerned that if he discloses the truth, Leon might stop physical therapy and impede the chance of any progress. Steven's goal is to maximize Leon's potential for recovery.

Schema Activation/Response Question

What is the best way for Steven to help his patient?

Cultivating Professional Values

The APTA core values aim to promote good reasoning. The key values at stake in Steven's story include:

- **Altruism:** sacrificing for others and putting others' needs before your own
- **Collaboration:** working together in pursuit of a shared goal
- **Compassion/Caring:** having kindness and finding importance in the suffering of others
- **Integrity:** acting in accord with one's personal and professional moral identity

Introduction to the Topic

Clinicians have duties to their patients. Providers must fulfill their fiduciary obligations, acting in the best interest of their patients. They are expected to provide care, respect autonomy, and commit to honesty. In the spirit of such duties, do physical therapists have a responsibility to encourage their patients to hope? This unit explores the nature and value of hope and whether clinicians have a duty to foster hope. The readings discuss competing views on hope and examine hope's role in the patient encounter.

Introduction to the Readings

The Nature of Hope and Hope in Clinical Practice

What is Hope?

Before we begin to examine the role of hope in the healthcare setting, we must ask ourselves, "What is hope?" Hope's complicated nature is preserved in the first reading, "Work and Days," the myth of Pandora as told by the ancient Greek poet Hesiod. According to Hesiod, the Olympian god Zeus wanted to punish Prometheus for stealing fire from the gods and giving it to humans. Zeus wanted to maintain the power of the gods and "keep hidden from men the means of life." By withholding fire, Zeus could ensure that humans remain powerless and weak. Against the authority of Zeus, Prometheus, a Titan, gave humans fire because he wanted to empower them.

In order to punish Prometheus for his transgressions, Zeus and the rest of the Olympian gods created Pandora, the first mortal woman. Zeus offered Pandora as a gift to Epimetheus, the brother of Prometheus. Epimetheus was enamored with Pandora's great beauty and forgot Prometheus's advice to never accept gifts from the gods. Epimetheus and Pandora married and at the wedding, the gods gave Pandora many gifts. Of particular interest, she received a jar that contained all of the evils and diseases of the world.

Hesiod tells us that one day Pandora opened the jar and the evils spilled out. Pandora quickly sealed the jar and managed to keep hope inside. Hesiod never explains why hope persisted in the jar. Further, Hesiod himself does not reveal the nature of the hope that remained.

Hesiod's story attempts to explain the suffering in the world. The myth of Pandora is a powerful vehicle for capturing how hope stays with us; it offers us insights about the human condition. However, myths are often interpreted within a cultural framework and in relation to social and community standards and norms. Some scholars interpret the myth to show that hope is a blessing, the greatest gift saved for humankind. In contrast, others infer from Pandora's tale that hope is a curse, the greatest evil saved for humankind. As a part of the human condition, is hope a blessing or a curse?

In the second reading, "Hope," we examine the German philosopher Friedrich Nietzsche's views on hope. In his book *Human, All Too Human*, Nietzsche recounts Hesiod's story of Pandora to illustrate why hope is bad for humanity. Nietzsche explains how Zeus intended for humans to have hope in order to punish them for receiving the gift of fire. He tells us that hope's persistence in the jar is a curse. Hope promotes human suffering. When humans hope, they prolong their misery.

Nietzsche describes how hope erodes the human spirit. Nietzsche tells us that hope provides a false sense of security and promotes self-deception. Indeed, Nietzsche acknowledges that "because of this power that hope has of making the suffering hold out, the Greeks regarded it as the evil of evils, as the most *malign* of evils; it remained behind [in Pandora's jar] as the source of all evil." Nietzsche's scathing critique suggests that hope can mislead us, and thus, we ought to be careful when practicing hope. In spite of his criticism, he also tells us that hope is an inherent part of the human condition. Humans, he claims, are vulnerable and weak and are engaged in a life of constant hardship and turmoil. Nietzsche cautions us to be wary of hope because hope enables us to envision the possibility of a better life even though life is inevitably tragic.[1] A recognition of the tragedy of life reveals hope's essential nature.

The third set of readings, selections from *Summa Theologica*, introduces a view of hope espoused by Christian theologian and philosopher St. Thomas Aquinas. In contrast to Nietzsche's bleak description, Aquinas defends the value of hope. Aquinas explains that, like all of our human faculties, the capacity to hope is the result of God's grace. Aquinas describes the four characteristic conditions of hope. First, the object of hope is something good; we do not hope for evil. Second, the object of hope is in the future; we do not hope for what is in the past. Third, the object of hope must be arduous and difficult to attain; we do not hope for what is easily within our power. Fourth, the object of hope is possible to obtain, though uncertain; we do not hope for what we know is certain.

In his analysis, Aquinas distinguishes between the passion of hope and the virtue of hope. Passions are nonrational capacities located in the sensitive part of the soul. Passions incline us to act in response to our environment; passions need to be jumpstarted by external objects and events. These objects and events, however, may be good or bad based on our perceptions of the external world.[2] In this way, passions may mislead us. Nonetheless, as passions are not regulated, they manifest our freedom. Aquinas claims that hope is a passion because as a nonrational capacity of the soul, it moves us to pursue what we perceive is a possible future good that is difficult to attain.

As a virtue, hope is a stable habit of will that oversees and regulates the passions. Hope is one of three cardinal theological virtues and is situated in between faith and love. Virtues, according to Aquinas, are guided by reason and the intellect; virtues thus direct a person toward the fulfillment of good. Virtues, unlike the passions, are not passive. Virtues are active because they are dispositions

---

[1] Alan Mittelman, *Hope in a Democratic Age* (New York: Oxford University Press, 2009).

[2] Michael Lamb, "Aquinas and the Virtues of Hope: Theological and Democratic," *Journal of Religious Ethics* 44, no. 2 (2016): 305–309.

of character and have both emotional and intellectual dimensions. Humans do not choose what passions will move them. However, humans choose to cultivate virtue in pursuit of becoming good. Virtues are good for us; they help us to achieve happiness. Hope enables us to see the possibility of the good in spite of the obstacles.

Contemporary scholars continue to investigate hope's nature and value. Hope is characterized in a variety of ways: as an emotion, a passion, a psychological habit of mind, and a virtue. According to the standard definition, hope involves a desire for an outcome combined with the belief that the outcome is possible yet uncertain.[3] This orthodox conception is reminiscent of Aquinas's account—albeit more secularized. Recently, though, this standard model has come under scrutiny. Some current scholars allege that the desire-belief formulation of hope fails to capture the richness of both the concept and the experience of hoping. For example, contemporary philosopher Luc Bovens criticizes the inadequacy of the standard definition. He claims it fails to capture the cognitive features involved in hoping.[4] Hope encompasses more than a desire for an end and a belief in possibility. Hope also comprises how we cognitively connect with our beliefs in relation to our goals; notably, hope "counteracts risk aversion" and "spawns more attainable constitutive hopes."[5] Bovens builds on the desire-belief model and incorporates a cognitive component—namely, "mental imaging"—that he says is active in the process of hoping.[6]

Similarly, present-day philosopher Philip Pettit argues that the standard model is superficial and glosses over the complexity of hope.[7] Pettit defends the need for a more substantial account of hope, one that can make sense of "the adversity that life puts in our path."[8] He distinguishes meaningful hope from the trivial hopes of day-to-day life. Pettit describes how a robust understanding of hope reveals its deeper value beyond its ubiquitous presence in human life. Both understated and common, hope can enrich the human condition by helping one to "escape the grip of beliefs that are so bleak or so unstable that they reduce a subject to a helpless status."[9]

Contemporary philosopher Adrienne Martin builds upon Pettit's observations about profound and inconsequential hopes.[10] Martin criticizes the desire-belief model and also argues for a more robust account, one that captures paradigmatic cases of hoping—namely, "hopes against hope."[11] Martin claims that the person who hopes against hope "takes 1 percent as a reasonable basis for hoping against hope [but] doesn't thereby think of 1 percent as 25 percent, or anything like that—she simply sees

---

[3] J. P. Day, "Hope," *American Philosophical Quarterly* 6, no. 2 (1969): 89–102.

[4] Luc Bovens, "The Value of Hope," *Philosophy and Phenomenological Research* 59 (1999): 667–681.

[5] Bovens, "The Value of Hope," 670.

[6] Bovens, "The Value of Hope," 674.

[7] Philip Pettit, "Hope and Its Place in Mind," *Annals of the American Academy of Political and Social Science* 592 (2004): 152–165.

[8] Pettit, "Hope and Its Place," 162.

[9] Pettit, "Hope and Its Place," 165.

[10] Adrienne M. Martin, *How We Hope: A Moral Psychology* (New Jersey: Princeton University Press, 2014).

[11] Martin, *How We Hope*, 14.

1 percent as enough to go forward."[12] Martin's analysis further exposes the rich contours of hope and her account of long odds and perseverance is applicable to the healthcare setting.

The fourth reading, selections from "Defining Hope," by contemporary philosopher Stan van Hooft offers a comprehensive analysis of the components of hope. Van Hooft fleshes out eight features of hope and examines the bond between hope and agency. He defends hope's value and claims it is central to human agency because of the link between hope and action. Unlike a wish that is directed at impossible objects, hope motivates action. Like Aquinas, he further situates hope in the context of virtue, suggesting that hope can be cultivated and inculcated into our characters. Van Hooft reflects upon the ethical significance of hope in relation to our human limitations, specifically our inability to control the future as well as our "finite and fallible capacities." He states: "That we have to live within such limitations is what makes hope a virtue. To live within our limitations is of ethical value in that it is conducive to living life happily." Van Hooft's focus on hope and ethics makes his discussion clearly applicable to our overarching examination of hope in the healthcare setting.

The analyses presented by both classical and contemporary authors illuminate hope's muddled definition, and they expose its positive and negative sides. On the one hand, hope is a blessing when it sustains us and when we attain what we desire. On the other hand, hope is a curse when it disappoints us and when the future fails to develop the way we want. These sharply contrasting views of hope, however, shed light on a common feature: hope is a fundamental part and process of the human condition.

Hope and Autonomy: Do Clinicians Have a Duty to Foster Hope?

While the previous readings allow us to extrapolate ideas about the role of hope in healthcare practice, this section and the final reading, in contrast, explicitly connects the two. In spite of hope's dual nature, questions about hope constantly emerge in the healthcare environment, specifically in patient–provider relationships. Recall Steven's predicament. As a clinician, he has specific duties to his patients—notably, obligations to truth-telling, patient best interests, and autonomy. However, if Steven divulges the clinical facts, Leon may not continue therapy; future progress may end. On the other hand, if Steven withholds the full truth from Leon, he violates his patient's autonomy and his fiduciary obligations. Steven cannot know the future with absolute certainty, but he must be careful to avoid weakening—or violating—the bond of trust he has formed with Leon. Steven must confront his doubts about Leon's future and a question of hope surfaces.

Do clinicians have a responsibility to help patients cultivate hope? Providers want the best for their patients, and patients want to recover and heal. Clinicians and patients mutually work together toward a shared goal. However, sometimes ambiguity does not warrant a clear direction toward the goal.

Hope can have a positive impact on patients by encouraging them to persevere during a struggle. Hope can enhance patient autonomy by encouraging a positive attitude in the face of high stakes and

---

[12] Martin, *How We Hope*, 23.

low odds. When patients are vulnerable and threatened by illness, hope can help patients feel less helpless. To choose hope is to choose to act upon the power of one's agency.

Hope supports the relationship between clinicians and patients as they collaborate and pursue goals together. The promotion of autonomy benefits patients by helping them make choices consistent with their sense of self and their life goals. Similarly, the encouragement of hope is to help patients move forward in pursuit of goals consistent with their identity and values. Clinical encounters impose inevitable limits on patients' options, and clinicians can help patients by promoting an environment of hope. While hope is not a promise or guarantee of good things to come, the choice to hope can improve a patient's sustaining power. Hope gives us the ability to respond to a crisis when circumstances throw us off balance.

I wrote the final reading, "Hope and Autonomy," as an examination of hope in the patient encounter. I explore hope as a part of a clinician's fiduciary duty to patients. I begin with a concise analysis of hope, describing hope as an antidote to the uncertainty that people encounter in their lives. Drawing on Holocaust survivor Viktor Frankl's account of hope, I describe how hope is an effective strategy for patients to confront doubt. Healthcare providers have a duty to be honest with their patients, and they also have a duty to promote their patients' best interests. By helping patients learn to hope, I propose that providers can maneuver through the moments where conflicting duties and ambiguous information make both trust and best interest elusive.

Recall Steven's story. Given Leon's diagnosis and progress during therapy, the odds of a full recovery are slim. The low probability heightens the difficulty of Steven's decision. However, failure to disclose information is a violation of the obligation to respect the dignity of a person. Steven has a duty to promote Leon's best interests and respect his autonomy. If Steven does not disclose the facts of the situation to Leon, even with his best interests in mind, Steven forsakes his fundamental fiduciary obligations. While the odds are low, the stakes are high for Leon. Thus, Steven resolves to tell Leon the truth. He also chooses to encourage Leon to pursue his goals for recovery; he emboldens Leon to hope. Moreover, Steven expresses his own hope for Leon's successful recovery.

References

Bovens, Luc. "The Value of Hope." *Philosophy and Phenomenological Research* 59 (1999): 667–681.

Day, J. P. "Hope." *American Philosophical Quarterly* 6, no. 2 (1969): 89–102.

Lamb, Michael. "Aquinas and the Virtues of Hope: Theological and Democratic." *Journal of Religious Ethics* 44, no. 2 (2016): 300–332.

Martin, Adrienne M. *How We Hope: A Moral Psychology.* New Jersey: Princeton University Press, 2014.

Mittelman, Alan. *Hope in a Democratic Age.* New York: Oxford University Press, 2009.

Pettit, Philip. "Hope and Its Place in Mind." *Annals of the American Academy of Political and Social Science* 592 (2004): 152–165.

Selection from "Works and Days"

By Hesiod; Edited by Hugh G. Evelyn-White

....

(ll. 42–53) For the gods keep hidden from men the means of life. Else you would easily do work enough in a day to supply you for a full year even without working; soon would you put away your rudder over the smoke, and the fields worked by ox and sturdy mule would run to waste. But Zeus in the anger of his heart hid it, because Prometheus the crafty deceived him; therefore he planned sorrow and mischief against men. He hid fire; but that the noble son of Iapetus stole again for men from Zeus the counsellor in a hollow fennel-stalk, so that Zeus who delights in thunder did not see it. But afterwards Zeus who gathers the clouds said to him in anger:

(ll. 54–59) 'Son of Iapetus, surpassing all in cunning, you are glad that you have outwitted me and stolen fire—a great plague to you yourself and to men that shall be. But I will give men as the price for fire an evil thing in which they may all be glad of heart while they embrace their own destruction.'

(ll. 60–68) So said the father of men and gods, and laughed aloud. And he bade famous Hephaestus make haste and mix earth with water and to put in it the voice and strength of human kind, and fashion a sweet, lovely maiden-shape, like to the immortal goddesses in face; and Athene to teach her needlework and the weaving of the varied web; and golden Aphrodite to shed grace upon her head and cruel longing and cares that weary the limbs. And he charged Hermes the guide, the Slayer of Argus, to put in her a shameless mind and a deceitful nature.

(ll. 69–82) So he ordered. And they obeyed the lord Zeus the son of Cronos. Forthwith the famous Lame God moulded clay in the likeness of a modest maid, as the son of Cronos purposed. And the goddess bright-eyed Athene girded and clothed her, and the divine Graces and queenly Persuasion put necklaces of gold upon her, and the rich-haired Hours crowned her head with spring flowers. And Pallas Athene bedecked her form with all manners of finery. Also the Guide, the Slayer of Argus, contrived within her lies and crafty words and a deceitful nature at the will of loud thundering Zeus,

Hesiod and Homer, "Works and Days," *Hesiod, The Homeric Hymns, and Homerica*, ed. Hugh G. Evelyn-White, 1914.

and the Herald of the gods put speech in her. And he called this woman Pandora[1], because all they who dwelt on Olympus gave each a gift, a plague to men who eat bread.

(ll. 83–89) But when he had finished the sheer, hopeless snare, the Father sent glorious Argos-Slayer, the swift messenger of the gods, to take it to Epimetheus as a gift. And Epimetheus did not think on what Prometheus had said to him, bidding him never take a gift of Olympian Zeus, but to send it back for fear it might prove to be something harmful to men. But he took the gift, and afterwards, when the evil thing was already his, he understood.

(ll. 90–105) For ere this the tribes of men lived on earth remote and free from ills and hard toil and heavy sickness which bring the Fates upon men; for in misery men grow old quickly. But the woman took off the great lid of the jar[2] with her hands and scattered all these and her thought caused sorrow and mischief to men. Only Hope remained there in an unbreakable home within under the rim of the great jar, and did not fly out at the door; for ere that, the lid of the jar stopped her, by the will of Aegis-holding Zeus who gathers the clouds. But the rest, countless plagues, wander amongst men; for earth is full of evils and the sea is full. Of themselves diseases come upon men continually by day and by night, bringing mischief to mortals silently; for wise Zeus took away speech from them. So is there no way to escape the will of Zeus.

---

[1] The All-endowed.
[2] The jar or casket contained the gifts of the gods mentioned in l.82

Hope

By Friedrich Nietzsche; Translated by Alexander Harvey

71

Hope.—Pandora brought the box containing evils and opened it. It was the gift of the gods to men, a gift of most enticing appearance externally and called the "box of happiness." Thereupon all the evils, (living, moving things) flew out: from that time to the present they fly about and do ill to men by day and night. One evil only did not fly out of the box: Pandora shut the lid at the behest of Zeus and it remained inside. Now man has this box of happiness perpetually in the house and congratulates himself upon the treasure inside of it; it is at his service: he grasps it whenever he is so disposed, for he knows not that the box which Pandora brought was a box of evils. Hence he looks upon the one evil still remaining as the greatest source of happiness—it is hope.—Zeus intended that man, notwithstanding the evils oppressing him, should continue to live and not rid himself of life, but keep on making himself miserable. For this purpose he bestowed hope upon man: it is, in truth, the greatest of evils for it lengthens the ordeal of man.

Friedrich Nietzsche, "Hope," *Human, All Too Human: A Book for Free Spirits*, trans. Alexander Harvey, 1908.

Selections from "Summa Theologica"

By St. Thomas Aquinas;
Translated by The Fathers of the English Dominican Province

First Part of the Second Part (FS) (QQ[1]–114)

Treatise On The Passions (QQ[22]–48)

Question 40

Article 1: Whether hope is the same as desire of cupidity?

Objection 1: It would seem that hope is the same as desire or cupidity. Because hope is reckoned as one of the four principal passions. But Augustine in setting down the four principal passions puts cupidity in the place of hope (De Civ. Dei xiv, 3,7). Therefore hope is the same as cupidity or desire.

Objection 2: Further, passions differ according to their objects. But the object of hope is the same as the object of cupidity or desire, viz. the future good. Therefore hope is the same as cupidity or desire.

Objection 3: If it be said that hope, in addition to desire, denotes the possibility of obtaining the future good; on the contrary, whatever is accidental to the object does not make a different species of passion. But possibility of acquisition is accidental to a future good, which is the object of cupidity or desire, and of hope. Therefore hope does not differ specifically from desire or cupidity.

On the contrary, To different powers belong different species of passions. But hope is in the irascible power; whereas desire or cupidity is in the concupiscible. Therefore hope differs specifically from desire or cupidity.

I answer that, The species of a passion is taken from the object. Now, in the object of hope, we may note four conditions. First, that it is something good; since, properly speaking, hope regards only

St. Thomas Aquinas, *Summa Theologica*, trans. The Fathers of the English Dominican Province, 1947.

the good; in this respect, hope differs from fear, which regards evil. Secondly, that it is future; for hope does not regard that which is present and already possessed: in this respect, hope differs from joy which regards a present good. Thirdly, that it must be something arduous and difficult to obtain, for we do not speak of any one hoping for trifles, which are in one's power to have at any time: in this respect, hope differs from desire or cupidity, which regards the future good absolutely: wherefore it belongs to the concupiscible, while hope belongs to the irascible faculty. Fourthly, that this difficult thing is something possible to obtain: for one does not hope for that which one cannot get at all: and, in this respect, hope differs from despair. It is therefore evident that hope differs from desire, as the irascible passions differ from the concupiscible. For this reason, moreover, hope presupposes desire: just as all irascible passions presuppose the passions of the concupiscible faculty, as stated above (Q[25], A[1]).

Reply to Objection 1: Augustine mentions desire instead of hope, because each regards future good; and because the good which is not arduous is reckoned as nothing: thus implying that desire seems to tend chiefly to the arduous good, to which hope tends likewise.

Reply to Objection 1: The object of hope is the future good considered, not absolutely, but as arduous and difficult of attainment, as stated above.

Reply to Objection 3: The object of hope adds not only possibility to the object of desire, but also difficulty: and this makes hope belong to another power, viz. the irascible, which regards something difficult, as stated in the FP, Q[81], A[2]. Moreover, possibility and impossibility are not altogether accidental to the object of the appetitive power: because the appetite is a principle of movement; and nothing is moved to anything except under the aspect of being possible; for no one is moved to that which he reckons impossible to get. Consequently hope differs from despair according to the difference of possible and impossible.

Question 40

Article 8: Whether hope is a help or a hindrance to action?

Objection 1: It would seem that hope is not a help but a hindrance to action. Because hope implies security. But security begets negligence which hinders action. Therefore hope is a hindrance to action.

Objection 2: Further, sorrow hinders action, as stated above (Q[37], A[3]). But hope sometimes causes sorrow: for it is written (Prov. 13:12): "Hope that is deferred afflicteth the soul." Therefore hope hinders action.

Objection 3: Further, despair is contrary to hope, as stated above (A[4]). But despair, especially in matters of war, conduces to action; for it is written (2 Kings 2:26), that "it is dangerous to drive people to despair." Therefore hope has a contrary effect, namely, by hindering action.

On the contrary, It is written (1 Cor. 9:10) that "he that plougheth should plough in hope ... to receive fruit": and the same applies to all other actions.

I answer that, Hope of its very nature is a help to action by making it more intense: and this for two reasons. First, by reason of its object, which is a good, difficult but possible. For the thought of its being difficult arouses our attention; while the thought that it is possible is no drag on our effort. Hence it follows that by reason of hope man is intent on his action. Secondly, on account of its effect. Because hope, as stated above (Q[32], A[3]), causes pleasure; which is a help to action, as stated above (Q[33], A[4]). Therefore hope is conducive to action.

Reply to Objection 1: Hope regards a good to be obtained; security regards an evil to be avoided. Wherefore security seems to be contrary to fear rather than to belong to hope. Yet security does not beget negligence, save in so far as it lessens the idea of difficulty: whereby it also lessens the character of hope: for the things in which a man fears no hindrance, are no longer looked upon as difficult.

Reply to Objection 2: Hope of itself causes pleasure; it is by accident that it causes sorrow, as stated above (Q[32], A[3], ad 2).

Reply to Objection 3: Despair threatens danger in war, on account of a certain hope that attaches to it. For they who despair of flight, strive less to fly, but hope to avenge their death: and therefore in this hope they fight the more bravely, and consequently prove dangerous to the foe.

Second Part of the Second Part (SS) (QQ[1]–189)

Treatise on The Theological Virtues (QQ[1]–46)

Question 17

Article 1: Whether hope is a virtue?

Objection 1: It would seem that hope is not a virtue. For "no man makes ill use of a virtue," as Augustine states (De Lib. Arb. ii, 18). But one may make ill use of hope, since the passion of hope, like the other passions, is subject to a mean and extremes. Therefore hope is not a virtue.

Objection 2: Further, no virtue results from merits, since "God works virtue in us without us," as Augustine states (De Grat. et Lib. Arb. xvii). But hope is caused by grace and merits, according to the Master (Sent. iii, D, 26). Therefore hope is not a virtue.

Objection 3: Further, "virtue is the disposition of a perfect thing" (Phys. vii, text. 17,18). But hope is the disposition of an imperfect thing, of one, namely, that lacks what it hopes to have. Therefore hope is not a virtue.

On the contrary, Gregory says (Moral. i, 33) that the three daughters of Job signify these three virtues, faith, hope and charity. Therefore hope is a virtue.

I answer that, According to the Philosopher (Ethic. ii, 6) "the virtue of a thing is that which makes its subject good, and its work good likewise." Consequently wherever we find a good human act, it must correspond to some human virtue. Now in all things measured and ruled, the good is that which attains its proper rule: thus we say that a coat is good if it neither exceeds nor falls short of its proper measurement. But, as we stated above (Q[8], A[3], ad 3) human acts have a twofold measure; one is proximate and homogeneous, viz. the reason, while the other is remote and excelling, viz. God: wherefore every human act is good, which attains reason or God Himself. Now the act of hope, whereof we speak now, attains God. For, as we have already stated (FS, Q[40], A[1]), when we were treating of the passion of hope, the object of hope is a future good, difficult but possible to obtain. Now a thing is possible to us in two ways: first, by ourselves; secondly, by means of others, as stated in Ethic. iii. Wherefore, in so far as we hope for anything as being possible to us by means of the Divine assistance, our hope attains God Himself, on Whose help it leans. It is therefore evident that hope is a virtue, since it causes a human act to be good and to attain its due rule.

Reply to Objection 1: In the passions, the mean of virtue depends on right reason being attained, wherein also consists the essence of virtue. Wherefore in hope too, the good of virtue depends on a man's attaining, by hoping, the due rule, viz. God. Consequently man cannot make ill use of hope which attains God, as neither can he make ill use of moral virtue which attains the reason, because to attain thus is to make good use of virtue. Nevertheless, the hope of which we speak now, is not a passion but a habit of the mind, as we shall show further on (A[5]; Q[18], A[1]).

Reply to Objection 2: Hope is said to arise from merits, as regards the thing hoped for, in so far as we hope to obtain happiness by means of grace and merits; or as regards the act of living hope. The habit itself of hope, whereby we hope to obtain happiness, does not flow from our merits, but from grace alone.

Reply to Objection 3: He who hopes is indeed imperfect in relation to that which he hopes to obtain, but has not as yet; yet he is perfect, in so far as he already attains his proper rule, viz. God, on Whose help he leans.

Selections from "Defining Hope"

By Stan van Hooft

W hat do we mean by "hope"? Hope seems to be a psychological state that we experience as part of our inner, subjective lives. However, not all usages of the word designate a state of mind in this way. We sometimes say of someone that "he does not have a hope". Suppose a goal kicker of average ability is taking a penalty kick against a team and a goalkeeper who are very skilled at football. As he is about to take his kick we might say of him that he has no hope of scoring the goal. We do not mean by this that he does not hope to score the goal. Indeed, we assume that he does hope to. But we are not referring to his psychological condition or to any mental states he might be in. We are referring to the objective fact that he has but a very slim chance of scoring a goal: so slim, in fact, that we think there is no likelihood at all that he will score a goal. We express this by saying that he has no hope of doing so. This statement is a description of the physical or factual likelihood of the outcome taking place. It is an assessment of the objective circumstances rather than of the internal psychological state of the footballer.

But the meaning that we are more interested in is when the word is being used to refer to the way someone feels or thinks about a situation. Let us explore this thoroughly.

An Example

John has to go out to attend a lecture at his university and he doesn't have an umbrella. Moreover, he is moving house and so most of his clothes are in boxes and relatively inaccessible. The weather forecast says there is a chance of rain and John does not want to get wet. Not only would getting wet be uncomfortable, but if his clothes get wet he will have nothing to wear the next day. As he is about to leave his house the sky is clear, but he can see dark clouds forming in the distance. John hopes that it will not rain.

What conditions have to obtain for it to make sense for John to hope that it will not rain? What are the thoughts and feelings that John needs to have for it to be appropriate for us to use the word "hope" in describing his state of mind?

The first thing that seems to be necessary is that he has a relevant desire. Indeed, he has a number of relevant desires. He desires to get to his university and he desires to do so at a certain time (with the consequence that he cannot wait for the weather to clear up). These desires flow from his commitment to his university studies. But his most relevant desire is the desire not to get wet. He would not enjoy walking to his destination in the rain. Indeed, in this case it is an unusually urgent desire since he does not have a change of clothes readily available to him. Accordingly, getting his clothes wet would not only be uncomfortable but would also be a serious inconvenience. John desires not to suffer this inconvenience. Moreover, not only does he need to have a desire that it not rain, but he has to be worried about the effect that the rain would have on him if it should come. He has to give thought to the unfortunate consequences to him of getting wet. Unlike Gene Kelly in the famous scene from the film *Singin' in the Rain,* John is anxious not to get wet. It is a matter of concern to him that his clothes stay dry so that he can wear them again the next day. The weather forecast, along with his seeing the dark clouds in the distance, only increases his anxiety about the possibility of getting wet.

A second condition is a consequence of the first. This is that John must consider it to be a good thing for him if it does not rain. It might not be good for farmers or gardeners who need rain, but given John's needs and concerns, he will judge it to be a good thing if it does not rain.

A third condition that needs to obtain for it to make sense for John to hope that it will not rain is that he has to consider it to be possible that it will rain. If John were convinced that it would not rain, there would be no point in his hoping that it would not. This condition is fulfilled in the example because he has heard a weather forecast that predicts that it will rain and because he has seen the dark clouds gathering in the distance. Notice that this is a psychological matter. It is not the objective possibility that it will rain that is important but the fact that he considers it possible. There are meteorological conditions that make it more or less likely that it will rain, and a certain set of meteorological conditions obtains on that day. According to the weather report those actual conditions are such as to make it likely that it will rain. On other days they might have been such as to make it very unlikely, if not impossible, that it would rain. These are objective conditions that are as they are irrespective of what John or anyone else thinks about them. What we are considering in the example, however, is what John considers possible or likely. One could imagine that if John were going out on a day when rain was extremely unlikely, he might still hope that it does not rain. But if he does have such a hope it will be because he thinks that rain is possible. If he were convinced that it was impossible that it would rain, then it would make no sense for him to hope that it would not. He would then not need to have such a hope because he already knows that it will not. But in this example he is envisaging an unwelcome possibility, that it will rain, and hoping that it will not eventuate. For him to hope that it will not happen he must consider it to be possible that it will.

A fourth condition for its making sense for John to hope that it will not rain is that it is possible that it will not rain. What this means is that if John knew that the meteorological conditions were such that rain was inevitable, then it would make no sense to describe John as hoping that it would not rain. If he hopes that it does not rain he must consider it possible that it does not rain. It follows that he must not think that rain is inevitable. If the conditions and indications were such as to induce in John the belief that rain was inevitable, it would make no sense for him to hope that it does not rain. This would be especially clear if we imagine John leaving the house when it is already raining. It certainly would not make sense for him then to hope that it does not rain. The technical term to describe the third and fourth conditions together—that the hoped-for event is possible but not inevitable—is the word "contingent". An occurrence is contingent if it might or might not have happened: that is, if it was not necessary, inevitable or impossible that it should happen. An occurrence is contingent if luck—in the form of unknown or unexpected causal influences—can intervene to make it happen or to stop it from happening.

The role of time in these conditions leads me to propose a fifth. As we have just noted, if John were to step outside and feel the rain on his skin it would make no sense for him to say "I hope it does not rain". It would be even stranger for him to say "I hope it is not raining". If it manifestly is raining, to say such a thing would be to misuse the word "hope". He might say "I wish it were not raining", but he could not say "I hope it were not raining". John's thought "I hope it does not rain" refers to the future. It might be more accurate to convey its content by saying "I hope it will not rain" and in this way make the future reference of the hope more explicit. But it is interesting to reflect that, from John's own point of view, anything is possible in the future. Even if the meteorological conditions were such that rain was completely inevitable, the fact that the rain is not yet actual gives John the psychological possibility of thinking that it might not come and hence of hoping that it will not. On the other hand, if time has passed so that that envisaged future is already settled, what was in John's future has become the present or the past. Accordingly, it will no longer be considered possible for things to turn out differently from the way they have. If the rain has started, it is no longer possible that it not be raining. It follows that it would make no sense for John to hope that it will not rain. If it ever does make sense to say "I hope it is not raining" when it actually is raining, we could imagine it doing so when John does not know whether it is raining as he is about to leave the house. In this case his hope is future oriented in his thinking if not in fact. What is objectively the case in the present is indeed the case. It is either raining or it is not. But John does not know whether it is. He will find out as soon as he steps outside. His stepping outside is still in the future, however, and so it makes sense for him to hope that it is not raining. In this case, he is hoping that what he finds out about the weather when he steps outside is that it is not raining.

What we have learnt from this example is that hopes are oriented toward the future. Suppose it had rained yesterday and that John had been out in the rain and his clothes had become wet. This had been a discomfort and inconvenience to him. Would it make sense for him now to hope that it had not rained yesterday? No, it would not. If it happened yesterday then he cannot now hope that the circumstances had been different. We saw above that it only makes sense to speak of hope if what is hoped for is possible. But yesterday's weather cannot be different now from what it was. It has happened in the past and cannot now be changed. That it did not rain yesterday is therefore impossible now. And if it is impossible, John cannot be said to hope for it.

This is not to say, however, that John cannot have some kind of feeling towards yesterday's weather that is, perhaps, similar to hope. He can wish that it had not rained yesterday, just as he can wish that it were not raining now when it actually is. The conditions for making sense of this are similar to the conditions that make sense of hope. He has a desire that it does not rain and that he does not get his clothes wet. And, in light of the science of meteorology, it is objectively possible that it might not have rained yesterday, even though, in fact, it did. But it is not now possible that it will not have rained yesterday because, in fact, it did. The feeling that John can have today that is similar to hope but different from it, is that he can wish that it had not rained yesterday.

A wish is a psychological state that is similar to a hope in interesting ways. Both are expressions of what John wants and of what he is anxious about. John wants to walk outside without getting wet and is anxious about ruining his clothes. He expresses this by feeling and articulating various wishes and hopes. With reference to the future he hopes that it will not rain, while with reference to the past he wishes that it had not rained. Hope refers to the future while, in this case, John's wish refers to the past. As I noted above, he could also wish that it were not raining in the present. If it is actually raining now, he could wish that it were not. But he cannot be said to hope that it not raining when it actually is raining since that would be hoping for something that, given present meteorological conditions, is never going to happen. Hopes can only refer to what is possible in the future.

Of course, wishes can refer to the future also. Let us imagine that when John steps outside and sees the dark clouds gathering he becomes convinced that rain is inevitable. He now considers it impossible that it will not rain. Accordingly, the fourth condition for its making sense for him to hope that it will not rain is not met. If he is completely convinced that it will rain, he cannot hope that it will not. Nevertheless, it would make sense to say of him that he wishes it would not rain. Even if he were to feel the first drops of rain on his clothes, he could go on wishing that it would not rain. His wishes can extend into the future and embrace any scenario. His hopes, however, are limited to what is possible, and if it is actually raining then it is no longer possible that it is not raining now. Accordingly, he cannot hope that it does not rain.

We can describe this difference between hopes and wishes in more general terms. We could say that wishes do not need to be realistic while hopes do. Just how realistic hopes should be is a matter we shall explore later. For the moment it is important to see that wishes need not be realistic at all. Not only can John wish that it not rain even when it manifestly is raining, but he can also wish that it had not rained yesterday when it clearly did. More generally, John can wish that the tooth fairy will stop it from raining or that the Easter bunny will bring him good luck. He can wish that global warming was not a reality or that dire poverty in the developing world was not the cause of millions of avoidable deaths every year. He can wish that he was rich or a champion footballer. In short, he can wish for the realization of any of his fantasies, the alleviation of all his anxieties, the satisfaction of all his desires and the fulfilment of all his ideals. But he can only hope for what he considers possible.

A sixth condition is implicit in what we have seen already. Given that it might or might not rain and that John does not know whether it will, we could say that he is uncertain about whether it will rain. Whether it will rain or not is an objective matter. Given the meteorological conditions and the laws of nature, it will either rain or it will not. The occurrence of rain is objectively contingent. But corresponding to this objective state of affairs there is the subjective state of John's not knowing whether it will rain or not. He is uncertain about the weather. It is this uncertainty, together with his anxiety about not getting wet, that leads him to hope that it will not rain.

There is also a seventh condition. Suppose John had an umbrella. We have already noted that he wants to keep dry when he goes outside and that he is anxious about getting his clothes wet. Let us qualify this a little by saying that he wants to keep relatively dry, or as dry as using an umbrella would make him. If this were what he wanted and if he had an umbrella, then it would be within his power to secure what he wants and allay his concerns when he goes outside in the rain. He just needs to put up his umbrella. In this circumstance, does it make sense for him to hope that it will not rain? Perhaps this question will gain more focus if we reformulate it as: would he hope that he will not get wet? (It was, after all, because he did not want to get wet that he hoped it would not rain in the original scenario.) I think it would not make very much sense for him to hope that he would not get wet because he has it within his power to ensure that he does not get wet. He only has to put up his umbrella. If he can control his circumstances in such a way as to avoid an unpleasant outcome or to secure a pleasant outcome, then it makes little sense for John to merely hope for that outcome. Rather, his mental state should be that of intending to secure that outcome. He could just go ahead and do what was necessary. To say that he hopes for that outcome implies that he cannot control all the parameters of the situation so as to secure the outcome he wants. To say that John hopes that he will not get wet implies that he cannot control whether or not he gets wet. If he can control it by using his umbrella, then it would be redundant for him to also hope not to get wet. (Once again, however, he could still wish that he not get wet, even as he is putting up his umbrella. The notion of a wish seems much more accommodating.)

To return to the original example in which John did not have an umbrella, we can apply this point by suggesting that a further condition for its making sense for John to hope that it would not rain is that he has no control over whether it rains or not. This point is easily missed in this example because no one has any significant control over meteorological conditions. The forces of nature that are involved here are too great and amorphous to admit of human control (although climate scientists do hope that there are things human beings can do to reduce the effects of global climate change). It is certainly true that no one can control whether it will rain today, least of all John himself. It is because he knows that he cannot control whether it rains or not that it makes sense for him to hope that it will not rain. If he were to be able to control the weather he would not need to hope for that outcome: he could just do what was necessary to secure it.

Let us summarize, then, the conditions that make it appropriate for John to hope that it does not rain in the circumstances I have described.

1. John has to be concerned about the effect of rain on him. This applies because he has a desire not to get wet.

2. John has to consider that it would be a good thing for him if it did not rain. (This follows from the first condition.)

3. He has to consider that it is possible that it will rain.

4. He has to consider that it is possible that it will not rain: that is, that rain is not inevitable.

5. The hope is directed towards weather conditions that lie in John's future.

6. John is uncertain about whether it will rain.

7. John is not able to control the meteorological forces that would stop it from raining.

Do these conditions allow us to offer a definition of what hope is? They certainly give us some clues as to what clauses should appear in such a definition. [...]

Hope and Action

Our attempts at distinguishing hopes from wishes have suggested a close link between hope and action, a link that is absent in the case of mere wishes. It is through action that we change the world so that it fits with our desires and hopes. If we want something we are motivated to do something to obtain it. Is it also the case that if we hope for something we are motivated to do something to obtain it? We have seen that if we wish for something we are not necessarily motivated to do something to obtain it because we may be engaged only in wishful thinking. So what about hope? We have discussed two examples that speak differently to this issue. John hoped that it would not rain. In his case there was nothing he could do to bring that eventuality about and so his hope did not lead to the kind of action that would stop it from raining. Christine Collins hoped that she might find her son. In her case there was something—albeit a very minimal something—she could do: be on the lookout for him. In the film she pursued this course of action even at the cost of missing social and possible romantic opportunities that came her way. In both cases it seemed appropriate to describe the relevant psychological state as one of hope. Is it, then, an essential element in hope that it leads to action or is a hope where no action is possible also a genuine case of hope? It seems that the relations between hope and action are complex.

One contemporary philosopher, Patrick Shade, defines hope as "the active commitment to the desirability and realizability of a certain end" (Shade 2001: 70). The first point inherent in this definition is that every action has an end or a goal. The second point is that the end or goal that we pursue must seem desirable to us. This does not entail that it must be pleasant, but we must see it as something that we want to achieve for some reason or other. It may be important or frivolous, morally required or morally neutral, pleasant or unpleasant, but we must have some cogent reason for pursuing it. We engage in an action in order to attain that goal. In cases where the goal is not impossible but difficult to reach because of some difficulty or obstruction we need strong motivation so that we are prepared to make the needed effort. We need commitment to our goal. According to Shade, hope is the form that this commitment takes. As he puts it, "hope has as its object an end (whether a thing or an event) whose realization lies beyond our present agency; that end may be remote or directly obstructed, yet insofar as we hope for it, we nevertheless remain committed to pursuing its realization" (*ibid.*: 3). He argues that our hopes sustain us when our ends do not seem realizable and that they are in that sense productive and expansive. This stress on commitment suggests that hope is an attitude towards the course of action that the agent is embarking on when that course of action includes difficulties and challenges. But Shade also speaks of "active" commitment. This suggests, in turn, that it is not just the attitude that is important but also the way we put that attitude into effect. Indeed, Shade goes so far as to define hope as an activity. As he puts it, "Hope is pragmatically conceived not as a private mental state, but as an activity belonging to an organism in dynamic relation with its environment. Hope, then, should be treated as an activity, as hop*ing*" (*ibid.*: 14).

But this account of hope as commitment and activity is problematic in John's example. John hopes that it will not rain, but there is nothing he can do to bring that state of affairs about. The problem here is that its not raining is not a goal of John's action. His goal is to get to university without getting wet. It not raining is a state of affairs that he is concerned should obtain, but it is not a goal that he can pursue. Not only can he not do anything to prevent it from raining, but he cannot conceive of it not raining as a goal or an end that he could pursue. It is not up to him whether it rains or not. Christine Collins, on the other hand, does have a goal: finding her son. This is an exceedingly difficult goal to achieve and all the indications are that it is unattainable. Nevertheless, she maintains her commitment to it and does what little she can to attain it. Hers is a paradigm example of what Shade understands hope to be.

Shade was not the first philosopher to see hope as closely connected to action. As we saw in the Introduction, Aquinas defined hope as the desire to act in pursuit of a future good that is arduous and difficult—but nevertheless possible—to obtain. If what is hoped for is conceived as the goal of an action that differs from others goals of action in that it is arduous and difficult but possible to obtain then there seems to be an inextricable link between hope and action. While this conception of hope is different from the one I have been developing, it seems to have some plausibility. It seems intuitively clear that whenever we act we hope for the outcome our action pursues. If I am walking to the university, then it could be said that I hope to get there. If I am putting on my socks, then it could be said that I hope to be wearing my socks. The reason these examples do not sound immediately apt is that these are actions the goals of which are very easy to achieve. I set about the task and I achieve it as a matter of course. I do not have to overcome any obstructions. While it is obvious that I intend to get to university or to put on my socks, respectively, I would not normally describe myself as hoping to achieve these things. This is because there is no difficulty in achieving them. There seems to be no gap, no uncertainty or no hindrance between forming the intention to do such things and actually doing them and achieving the intended outcome. The element of arduousness or difficulty that Aquinas points to is absent. On the other hand, if I take on something difficult—lifting a heavy load in the gymnasium, for example—I might indeed be self-consciously hoping that I achieve the goal. I form the intention but my agency does not just flow through to the action to put that intention immediately into effect. My action does not flow through smoothly to the attainment of my goal. There is a difficulty that I am aware of and I respond to that difficulty by hoping that I succeed. I should also respond to that difficulty by making an effort to succeed. If there are steps I could take to make success more likely—by using the correct lifting techniques, for example—then I should take them. But I am aware that the task is a challenging one and that my efforts may not be adequate to the task. Accordingly, I do not only intend to lift the weight or make the strenuous effort; I also find myself hoping that I will succeed.

Shade and Aquinas have captured an important point: that hope accompanies action, especially in cases where there is some difficulty in achieving what one intends to achieve. There are many examples where intending to do something and beginning to do it do not guarantee success. One must make an effort or be persistent. One must continue on despite setbacks. One must face dangers or difficulties with courage or determination. One must be resourceful or strategic. In all such cases one will do more than just intend to achieve the outcome and set about the task. One will also hope to succeed. Hope will be necessary here as a motivator for the effort required to attain the goal.

But there is a sense in which this applies to all actions, even ones that are not difficult. Even when I am putting on my socks it is possible—although extremely unlikely—that I will hurt my back in such a way that I am not able to bend down enough to complete the task. Even when I am walking to university it is possible—although very unlikely—that I will be hit by a car and prevented from completing my journey. Although these mishaps are unlikely, they are possible, and that possibility introduces an element of uncertainty or even risk into my life as an agent. Every action that I set out to perform is accompanied by an element of anxiety—however small—as to whether I shall be able to achieve what I set out to achieve. This anxiety may be vanishingly mild in the case of putting on my socks, but it will be more present to me in the case of lifting the weight. In more complex actions or courses of action, such as working towards a university degree or bringing up my children, this anxiety will be an ever-present element of doubt, concern and uncertainty that will both enliven and darken my involvement in those courses of action. I can never be sure of success. There is a multitude of circumstances or events that could frustrate my efforts and undermine my achievements. In the face of all this I will need determination, courage, commitment and endurance. What will motivate these stances if not hope for success?

When discussing the psychological states that accompany action most philosophers concentrate on the intentions that lead us to act. According to their account, every deliberate action is directed, as it were, by an intention that I have. I might not always be conscious of this intention, but if I were asked why I am putting on my socks, for example, I would have an answer. My actions have goals which I can bring to mind if I need to. It is this which defines these events as actions, as opposed to reactions or reflex movements. If what I am doing is performing an action then, by definition, I am pursuing a goal, and I have the intention of attaining that goal. In this way intentions are inextricable from actions. However, my suggestion is that there is at least one more element involved: hope. I not only intend to achieve my goal but I also hope to. This hope will be more present to my self-awareness when the action or course of action is difficult or risky, but I would suggest that it is present in a non-explicit way even in simple actions that are easy to perform. Between the intention and the successful completion of the action there is always room for bad luck to intervene. I may put my back out reaching down to put on my socks. I may have my studies interrupted by a death in my family. My children may suffer illness. There is always a gap between our intentions and the achievement of what we intend, which our efforts may not overcome. There is always the possibility of failure. Our intentions cannot bridge this gap. We do not have complete control over our circumstances. Accordingly, our hoping bridges the gap. This will be clear and apparent in cases where the gap looms large—as when the task is arduous and difficult—but it is also the case even when the action is easy and routine. Fate can always intervene and frustrate our intentions. Deep down we know this and, accordingly, deep down we supplement our intentions with hope.

As Aquinas suggests, when we set out on an arduous or difficult course of action, we hope to achieve our goal. This hope accompanies our intention and our agency. In so far as we cannot be sure of success, we hope for it. My suggestion is that, at an implicit and deep level of our consciousness, this structure of hope accompanies all our actions because of our implicit and deep awareness of our vulnerability to bad luck and mishap. Hope is our existential response to the contingency that is a mark of all our actions and of the world we live in.

Of course we can also respond to this contingency by taking care when we act, by making the required effort and by planning. Planning is often required in a course of action. By ensuring that we have prepared for our action by, for example, acquiring the right tools, engaging in the right training, or dividing up the task into its constituent parts we can be more assured of success. In this way planning is an important preparation for action and, in so far as it gives us some assurance of success, lessens the need for hope. Indeed, it is interesting to note that planning is similar to hope in that it is directed towards the future and what is possible but contingent. Moreover, it is motivated by a desire for success and, sometimes, by anxiety about failure. Yet it differs from hope in that it is an attempt to control the circumstances of one's action and the means at one's disposal so as to ensure a successful outcome, while hope becomes relevant when we recognize that our control has limits. It is when we see that, despite our planning and preparation, success is not certain that we find ourselves hoping for it. John's situation is an extreme example of this. In his case, there is nothing he can do to control the weather. Accordingly, the only psychological state that is available to him when he does not want to get wet is to hope that it does not rain.

So far we have been discussing how hope contributes to our agency: how it accompanies our actions because we intuitively know that our efforts may not be effective enough to realize our intentions and goals. But there is also another question that has arisen for us in the example of Christine Collins: is it necessary for hope to be expressed in action? Is hope that does not lead to action somehow incomplete and, as such, not a genuine case of hope?

Perhaps we should consider a further example here. Tony is a young man studying at the university who describes himself as hoping to go to South America to teach English there after he graduates. But at this present time he is doing nothing to realize this hope. He is studying, certainly, and this can contribute to the attainment of what he hopes for, but he has formed no specific plan to go to South America at any specific time and his course of study is not directly or deliberately designed to give him the qualifications needed to teach English in a Spanish-speaking country. In the absence of a purposeful course of action designed to realize his hope, we might be tempted to say that he merely wishes to go to South America: that he is engaged in wishful thinking. If he genuinely hopes to go, we would expect to see—if not now, then in the near future—some activity on his part designed to realize that goal. Can Tony hope for that goal without also intending to achieve it and acting to bring it about? Is hope a psychological state that is distinct from action or are we inclined to say that if Tony hopes for something that he could achieve by setting out on a course of action to achieve it, then his hope is empty or inauthentic if he does not set out on that course of action? We would not say that he hoped to go to South America if he were just waiting for a chance event to occur, such as winning the lottery so that he could pay the costs of going. Perhaps it is enough if he thinks that, at some future time, he will set about doing what he needs to do in order to travel to South America. For the moment he is concentrating on his studies and not forming any plans. But he has a vague and non-specific intention to do something about it in due course. And this vague idea that he has about his future could be described as his hoping that he will go. He is not unaware that he will need to do something about it at some time, but he does not feel ready to do so yet. For the moment he only hopes that he will go to South America.

The concept of hope has a slightly different meaning here. In this context, it is not the case that Tony hopes for an outcome because he knows that his efforts to attain that outcome are vulnerable to failure. Rather, he hopes for the outcome because he is not yet ready to embark on that project. At this stage going to South America is only a hope. It is not yet a plan or a project and it is not yet a specific intention. Indeed, it is probably fair to say that it is not very different from a wish and it may be that he has used the word in a misleading way when he described himself as hoping that he would go to South America. We could say that he wants to go to South America or that he wishes to but, in so far as he is not yet ready to take any action in order to achieve what he wants, we might not describe him as hoping that he will go. On the other hand, perhaps what he is hoping for is that circumstances will arise that will allow him to go. Some of these circumstances might be achievements of his, such as obtaining his university degree, while others will be due to others or to luck, such as his aunt giving him the money to go or his winning the lottery. The last two will be circumstances that are necessary for his going but are not under his control. Tony can only hope that, like the weather in John's case, these circumstances will come about. There are some things he can do to attain his goal, and he ought to set about doing them, but there are other circumstances that he can only hope will come about because they are not up to him.

These reflections lead me to disagree with Shade and Aquinas. For them, hopes, goals and actions are inextricably linked. Hope without action would be inauthentic. While there is some truth in this, I have argued that hope arises at precisely the point where agency leaves off. We entertain hope in respect of those conditions that are necessary for our achieving our goals but which we cannot bring about ourselves. Hope covers the gap between effort and outcome and where that gap is extremely small no hope is needed, while where it is huge hope is all we have. So in a case where we embark on an action that is simple to perform and of which the outcome is easily achieved, we have no need to hope that we will achieve that outcome, while in John's case, where there is nothing that he can do to achieve what he wants—that it will not rain—all he can do is hope for that eventuality. [...]

The Ethics of Hope

If we summarize what we have discovered thus far we will see that there are elements of ethical significance in hope. I have suggested that hopes are a subcategory of wishes for outcomes judged to be good, which differ from other wishes in that they are motivated by a degree of anxiety or concern about specific circumstances in the world and in that they are limited to what the person who hopes considers both possible and contingent. Oriented to an uncertain future that we cannot completely control, our hopes express our acknowledgement that whatever happens is limited by our finite and fallible capacities and by the laws of physics. There may be a prayer-like element of supplication in our hope but the risk that what we hope for might not happen is something we have to live with. That we have to live within such limitations is what makes hope a virtue. To live within our limitations is of ethical value in that it is conducive to living life happily.

Moreover, there are further ethical or normative elements in hope. It is a wish that differs from other wishes in that it should motivate us to appropriate action when that is possible. While wishes can stay in the realm of fantasy or daydream, hopes should lead us to take whatever action is available in order to pursue what we hope for. Taken together, the characteristics of hope that distinguish it from wishing show that hope involves an engagement with reality that wishing lacks. This engagement takes the form not only of being committed to any relevant actions that are available, but also of understanding what possibilities there are in the world for actions that would help us to realize our goals and what the likelihood is that we shall be able to do so. Unlike hoping, wishful thinking does not need to have regard for how the world is or for what is likely to occur in it. Hope needs to combine our desires, emotions, feelings and anxieties with beliefs about, and understandings of, the world. There is a cognitive dimension to hope that makes this psychological state amenable to rational appraisal. To hope for something requires that we make some assessment as to whether what we hope for is possible, likely or inevitable. We need to have an understanding of the world, of our place in it and of our social relationships. We need to understand and respect the laws of nature that science has disclosed to us. Accordingly, it is an ethical requirement that when we hope we ought to be realistic. If we are not realistic, we are likely to slip into wishful thinking.

Hope and Reason

While there is probably some cognitive aspect to most emotions, this point shows that hope is not an emotion in any simple or purely reactive manner. It involves a relatively high degree of understanding of the world intermingled with the concerns and desires that we have. If placing hope into the broader category of wishes suggested that it was an emotion, we should now modify that suggestion by adding that it also involves knowledge, belief and understanding. This, in turn, suggests that the distinction philosophers are fond of making between cognitive states such as belief and knowledge on the one hand, and emotional or motivational states such as desires and wishes on the other, is not as sharp as traditional thinking would suggest.

The reason that this distinction was made at all was that it allowed us to understand the internal struggles we often find ourselves with and to articulate the ethical problems we face in daily life. We often find ourselves not doing what we think we ought to do. We often find ourselves succumbing to temptations or shying away from our obligations. One way of understanding this is to suppose that, inside us, there is a struggle between reason and responsible thought on the one hand and unruly emotions and desires on the other. The paradigm case of an emotion in this model is anger. Anger seems to come over us like a turbulent storm and it causes us to lose our self-control and our ability to think clearly or act responsibly. Desire, too, can overwhelm us in this way. Accordingly, ancient thinkers such as Plato (c.428–c.348 BCE), Christian moral theologians and modern philosophers such as Kant have taught that we should seek to control our emotions and allow reason to rule our lives. The emotions were not to be trusted, while reason was infallible if used correctly and without interference from the unruly passions. Reason was to be the motivator of our actions, while emotional reactions were to be controlled or suppressed. The distinction between reason and cognitive states on one side, and emotions and desires on the other side, ties in with this moralistic conception of human existence. Accordingly, it is of considerable interest to note that hope straddles the distinction. It is both cognitive and motivational, rational and emotional, active and reactive.

This being the case, it is appropriate to ask whether hoping can be rational. If it were purely emotional or reactive and if the distinction between reason and emotion were a sharp one, then it would not be. But if it has a cognitive dimension it can be. We can explore whether it is appropriate for a person to hope for something by asking whether the understanding of the world and what is possible or likely in it that is implicit in the hope is correct or rationally justifiable. Accordingly, hope as a virtue has a further normative feature. We have already seen that it should lead to appropriate action when such actions are available. We can now add that it should be rational rather than naive.

However, some argue that hopes do not need to be rational: that it is valid to "hope against hope". The Christine Collins example shows that hope can be valid as an emotional anchor: something that we cling to regardless of circumstances, regardless of what our reason tells us is happening or going to happen, and regardless of whether our hope is rational or irrational. Christine is hoping for something that she knows is extremely unlikely: finding her lost son after many years. And yet it may not be irrational to want such an outcome and thus to hope for it, no matter how unlikely it is. The finding of the other missing boy, David, has shown Christine that it is possible that her Walter is still alive. In this way her finding him still seems possible, however unlikely it is, and her psychological state can be, by our definition, one of hope. But if the hope is unrealistic or misguided, the actions it inspires will be futile or even damaging. Christine shows a kind of sad nobility in never giving up, but after a certain amount of time—five, ten, or twenty years—that sort of active pursuit would cease to be rational. One could imagine a family being torn apart through not accepting that the search has at some point become futile: so much potential going into pointless actions, perhaps siblings living in the missing child's shadow. Sometimes, against all odds, the seemingly impossible happens, and the hope may turn out to be justified. But that is not an argument for the *rationality* of the hope.

So far we have agreed that it would be irrational to hope for something impossible since to do so would not be to hope but to engage in wishful thinking. On this view the less possible something is, the less rational it is to hope for it. But this does not seem to tell the whole story. Perhaps a rational assessment of possibility should not be the only criterion. After all, on those grounds it would seem irrational to hope for world peace or global justice. Christine Collins, whose child seems irrevocably lost but who goes on hoping, seems admirable even if not rational.

Perhaps the question of whether it is rational or irrational does not apply to the hope itself, but to the actions that hope inspires. Whether it is rational or irrational to hope that the child will be found, it will certainly be irrational to leave a place at the table for him each evening. In relation to Bob's lottery ticket, his hope that he wins is fairly irrational given the odds, but to spend the money he has not yet won would be an even more irrational action based on an irrational assessment of his chance of winning. On this view, although you cannot have an irrational hope, you can have an irrational assessment of your chances, and take irrational actions in response to the resulting expectations.

Nevertheless, to think of hope as a phenomenon that is outside the boundaries of rationality and as based on something distinct from rationality would be very problematic. On such a view, hope would be a specific form of wish while reasoning about the likelihood of the hoped-for outcome or about appropriate courses of action is a separate matter. On this view hope would be nothing more than an emotional anchor that can give us a break from our reason and rationality. [...]

Hope as a Virtue

We saw in the Introduction that Aristotle gives us a structure for thinking about virtues that might help us to understand hope further. We have just been exploring the cognitive and rational aspects of hope, which are relevant to seeing it as what Aristotle called an "intellectual virtue". But in the Introduction we also saw the way in which Aristotle understood the virtues that relate to our desires and emotions as states of mind that could be understood as occupying an appropriately moderate position between two relevant extremes. Given that hope also relates to our desires, emotions and anxieties, can this model be used to further explicate hope as a virtue? I would suggest that it can. Although I suggested that hope is not itself felt in differing degrees, it can make sense to describe it as being more or less intense depending on the other psychological states that contribute to it. Accordingly, hope can be situated in the middle of a spectrum of psychological states, at one end of which are states of excess and at the other end of which are states of deficiency. On this model, I would suggest that the extremes that virtuous hope avoids are presumption, resignation and despair.

Presumption is an excess of hope. It consists in being overconfident that the good outcome for which one hopes will come about. Presumption lacks the sense of uncertainty that is a defining characteristic of hope. This may lead the presumptuous person to make inadequate efforts in securing the desired good outcome on the grounds that he believes that things will turn out well whether or not he makes such efforts. Moreover, we can understand presumption as an excessive expression of the element of supplication that is inherent in hope. The presumptuous person is one who feels overly confident that whatever cosmic powers are out there are indeed on his side and are indeed in connivance with him, as Marcel had put it. Accordingly, those powers can be relied on to ensure that the desired outcome will occur. Indeed, an even more extreme form of such presumption is the feeling that one is entitled to the good outcome or deserves it in some way, either because one has been good or because one has placed trust in those powers or gods. Authentic hope would never go so far.

At the other end of the spectrum is despair: a deficiency of hope. Despair consists in not being able to hope because one has lost all confidence that things could turn out well. Not only does one feel certain that things will turn out for the worst, but, even more deeply, one is unable to commit to any judgement that a future state might be good for one. Nothing seems worth doing and no prospects of success seem to be on offer. Despair is the absence of hope. But if despair is the most deficient state in the spectrum of variations of hope, there is another state that could be identified on the deficient side of that spectrum, although it does not stand at its extreme end. This state is resignation. Resignation is an attitude that accepts that the desired good outcome that one had hoped for will not come about. It is an acceptance that things are not going to go one's way. One begins to think that the outcome is not possible and so hope fades. One no longer approaches the relevant circumstances in one's life with expectation and one no longer seeks—whether through supplication directed at others or through one's own efforts—the goods that one had hoped for. Accordingly, one gives up making an effort and the scope of one's world contracts a little. Life has less to offer and hope lies defeated.

As we move from the excess of presumption, through appropriate hope, and on to resignation and despair, we may suppose that the final state would be depression. However, I think of depression more as a psychological pathology than as an attitude that could be appraised in ethical terms. Depression is not a vice, but an illness. [...]

Hope and Autonomy

By Katherine K. Johnson

Introduction

To understand the role of hope in healthcare, we begin by examining the patient–provider relationship. Healthcare providers have an obligation to respect patient autonomy. This duty includes disclosing medical information and helping patients understand and interpret this information so that they can make decisions consistent with their life goals and values. I propose that supporting and respecting an ability to hope is an additional component of patient autonomy.

In this [reading], I examine hope's role in the patient encounter. I provide a basic framework for hope and assert that hope is an antidote to the uncertainty we encounter in our lives. I explore hope's ethical importance and examine this perspective in the context of clinicians' fiduciary duties to patients. My goal is to delineate the reasons why healthcare providers should nurture and inspire hope. I show that this clinical responsibility stems from fundamental professional commitments to act in the best interests of patients and to foster their autonomous decision-making capacities. Providers must respect patients' right to hope.

A Framework for Hope

People hope for a variety of reasons. Most people hope for things that will improve their lives and will make them feel happy or satisfied. The objects of hope vary. Some are probable, and some are merely possible. We hope for outcomes such as good weather, passing a test, enduring a challenge, or surviving an incurable disease. These all seem like reasonable scenarios to hope for, though we only control some (e.g., passing a test) and not others (e.g., good weather). Many perceive hope as valuable to the human condition. Others, however, view hope as a regrettable part of existence and dispute its alleged value and benefit. Undoubtedly, the nature of hope is complex, and no one formulation captures hope's complete essence.

On the one hand, hope can enable well-being. It can help us pursue admirable goals. It can facilitate human flourishing. On the other hand, hope can encourage intellectually defective practices. It can encourage false beliefs. It can be hurtful and lead to suffering. It can even be vicious when, for example, we hope bad outcomes befall others.

Even with this complicated nature, hope remains a familiar presence in healthcare. Patients hope to improve. Providers hope to heal. Clearly, these hopes differ from ordinary day-to-day hopes. They are not like fleeting desires for good weather. Rather, these hopes are vital; they are a critical response to the situations that test us and threaten our sense of our identities.

Hope has three essential aspects. First, hope involves a desire for an outcome. The affective aspect relates to hope's motivational dimension. This feature illuminates the emotional attitudes associated with hope. Second, hope includes a belief that the desired outcome is possible yet uncertain. The intellectual dimension of hope evaluates whether an outcome is possible. Hope differs from wish because hope is rooted in the reality of a situation; hope does not distort reality. Third, hope is tied to agency. The self-actualizing dimension of hope incorporates one's authentic self with the powers of one's agency. Hope promotes a person's sense of reflective agency by helping them to pursue their goals and to understand both their capacities and limits.[1] Various scholars have proposed different formulations of hope, yet many agree that these three components are essential to its nature.[2]

In his memoir *Man's Search for Meaning*, Viktor Frankl illustrates the significance of hope for survival.[3] Frankl, a Holocaust survivor, describes a model of hope that is appropriate to the healthcare setting because patients, like Frankl, must confront threatening events. Frankl's narrative highlights how hope can arise in times of uncertainty, especially when the stakes are high and the odds are low. Hope gives us the push we need to move toward an unknown future.

Frankl argues in favor of cultivating hope because of its life-sustaining qualities. For example, Frankl recounts the story of "F—" who was a fellow prisoner at Auschwitz. F— had a dream that foreshadowed when he would be liberated. The dream inspired F— to hope. As the day of the liberation that he dreamt of drew closer, no signs of rescue were present. F— was less hopeful and then fell ill. Frankl describes his observation:

---

[1] Victoria McGeer defends an agency-based account of hope. She argues that hope is a fundamental activity that unifies a person. See Victoria McGeer, "The Art of Good Hope," *Annals of the American Academy of Political and Social Science* 529 (2004): 100–127.

[2] Adrienne M. Martin, *How We Hope: A Moral Psychology* (Princeton, NJ: Princeton University Press, 2014); Luc Bovens, "The Value of Hope," *Philosophy and Phenomenological Research* 59 (1999): 667–681; Philip Pettit, "Hope and Its Place in Mind," *Annals of the American Academy of Political and Social Science* 592 (2004): 152–165; Stan van Hooft, *Hope* (New York: Routledge, 2011); Claudia Blöser and Titus Stahl, "Fundamental Hope and Practical Identity," *Philosophical Papers* 46, no. 3 (2017): 345–371.

[3] Viktor E. Frankl, *Man's Search for Meaning* (Boston: Beacon Press, 1959).

When F— told me about his dream, he was still full of hope. … But as the promised day drew nearer, the war news which reached our camp made it appear very unlikely that we would be free on the promised date. On March twenty-nineth, F— suddenly became ill and ran a high temperature. On March thirtieth, the day his prophecy had told him that the war and suffering would be over for him, he became delirious and lost consciousness. On March thirty-first, he was dead.[4]

Despite F—'s ultimate outcome, Frankl asserts that hope sustained F—. Frankl believed that choosing hope is better than dwelling on uncertainty, especially when the odds are not in one's favor. For Frankl, giving up hope is a reason for death.

While Frankl believed in the value of hope, he often struggled to have hope. In his autobiography, he describes the environment of the concentration camp as hopeless. Nevertheless, he claims one must not give up hope. On one especially low-morale day in the camp, Frankl tried to encourage his fellow prisoners: "I told them that although there was still no typhus epidemic in the camp, I estimated my own chances at about one in twenty. But I also told them that, in spite of this, I had no intention of losing hope and giving up. For no man knew what the future would bring, much less the next hour."[5] Frankl remarks that to hope in such a miserable place did not come naturally; hope took a lot of effort. Indeed, to surrender hope was to surrender one's self. The choice to hope was in his power.

Frankl teaches us that to choose hope is to exercise the powers of agency. We find the value of hope in realizing that we have the freedom to choose how we react to our circumstances. To choose hope amid a struggle is a challenge, but the choice to hope manifests our freedom. Hope is a facet of one's authentic self-governing capacities that we choose to ignite. Moreover, hope is an aspect of a person's integrity and character. Hope is a part of the human condition that strengthens the power of agency; we *choose* hope.

Frankl's narrative depicts the kind of hope that defines who we are. His account teaches us four important lessons about hope's meaning and value. First, choosing hope in the midst of a struggle is a mark of an agent's self-governing power. Second, hope provides an attitude of future possibility, a reason to move forward. Third, hope is an authentic expression of the self and illuminates a person's values and goals. Fourth, as the manifestation of personal freedom, hope demonstrates a person's strength of character. The power of hope lies in its ability to help us move forward in pursuit of the possibility of the good even when the odds are against us.

As we have seen with Viktor Frankl, a disposition of hope can promote an individual's exercise of autonomy, one's capacity of self-governance. While the comparison between a concentration camp and a hospital is imperfect, Frankl's account is instructive. He illustrates how hope is responsive to a crisis and reveals our capacities as agents. A crisis disrupts and jeopardizes our ability to see ourselves

---

[4] Frankl, *Man's Search for Meaning*, 70–71.
[5] Frankl, *Man's Search for Meaning*, 77.

as self-determining agents in control of our lives. To hope is to be reflective. Hope enables us to comprehend our environment, abilities, and limitations. Frankl teaches us that hope constitutes how we see ourselves because we often define ourselves through our choices. When people hope, they see possibility; they see themselves as agents with the power to pursue a goal.

The hope sketched out in Frankl's narrative is not optimism, though hope includes a positive attitude about future possibilities. Optimism is a bias hardwired in our brain, an inclination to overestimate the likelihood of the occurrence of positive events in the future and to underestimate negative events.[6] Both hope and optimism can help us to move forward, but hope involves the recognition of the good, whereas optimism does not. Hope involves character, while optimism involves habit.

Hope sustains us when we are confronted with doubt and uncertainty. Hope enables us to adapt to uncertainty. It furnishes us the power to choose how to react to a situation; it helps us to move forward or change course. Hope can help people live within the constraints that bind them.

Autonomy: A Basis for Hope

Respect for autonomy is one of the central principles in biomedical ethics. Autonomy articulates a standard of respect for the self-governing capacity of patients. Moreover, this ethical principle defines the interpersonal dynamic that must occur in the patient–provider interaction. Providers must respect patients' autonomous capacities and help them effectively exercise this capacity.

Contemporary bioethicists Tom Beauchamp and James Childress capture the prevailing account of autonomy and the obligations that arise:

> To respect autonomous agents is to acknowledge their right to hold views, to make choices, and to take actions based on their personal values and beliefs. Such respect involves respectful *action*, not merely a respectful *attitude*. It requires more than noninterference in others' personal affairs. It includes, in some contexts, building up or maintaining others' capacities for autonomous choice while helping to allay fears and other conditions that destroy or disrupt autonomous action.[7]

Beauchamp and Childress's account highlights the positive and negative obligations that emerge from respect for autonomy. Healthcare providers have a positive obligation to actively enhance and encourage a patient's ability to be an autonomous decision-maker. Clinicians also have a negative duty to avoid interfering with or curtailing a patient's freedom to make choices on their own behalf.

---

[6] Tali Sharot, *The Optimism Bias: A Tour of the Irrationally Positive Brain* (New York: Vintage Books, 2011).

[7] Tom L. Beauchamp and James F. Childress, *Principles of Biomedical Ethics*, 6th ed. (New York: Oxford University Press, 2009), 103.

The informed consent process is an example of these positive obligations. Patients must be competent to make decisions, must choose without coercion or duress, and must be fully informed about treatment options, benefits, and risks. However, informed consent is a process, and improving a patient's decision-making capacities does not involve a simple transaction and the sharing of information. Providers have a duty to help patients fully comprehend the nature of their medical diagnosis along with treatment options and their risks. Uncertainty and the lack of perfect knowledge, though, are two of the biggest obstacles to fulfilling one's duty to promote autonomy. While patients have the right to make decisions about their health, providers must help patients understand both the nature of their condition and their limitations. Further, providers' duty to autonomy extends beyond disclosing medical information. They also have a duty to promote patient agency, to encourage a patient to see themselves as someone with the power to choose their course in life.

The negative duties that relate to autonomy restrict what providers can do to patients. Providers must not interfere in the exercise of autonomy. For example, clinicians cannot lie to patients, and patients cannot be forced to undergo treatments against their will. Clinicians, however, cannot know the future, and ambiguous information can impede reliable diagnoses and treatment plans. Nonetheless, providers can maneuver around these obstructions and still work in the best interests of their patients. Providers can help patients better understand their options and limitations so they can exercise their agency. Providers must recognize the limits of human knowledge and within these constraints help their patients become effective decision-makers, individuals making choices that are in line with their own life plans and goals.

Despite the best efforts of providers, patients remain vulnerable. Injury, illness, and disease often hinder patients' control and ability to self-govern. In this context, hope can be an effective strategy for confronting uncertainty, doubt, and the barriers that threaten autonomy.

Respect for autonomy obliges healthcare providers to avoid infringing upon a patient's sense of personal power and agency. This duty does not require that clinicians always encourage hope, but they must not be a barrier to hope. Providers must recognize their role in promoting autonomous agency and helping patients regain some measure of control over their lives.

Conclusion: The Right to Hope

The experience of illness can undermine and threaten patient autonomy. Injury and disability combined with uncertainty can cause patients to distrust the world. In response, clinicians must help patients be effective decision-makers. The principle of respect for autonomy demands helping patients make a choice; it also involves understanding, gaining perspective, and knowing what patients value.

Enabling hope empowers agency. As a result, hope can enhance personal autonomy. Hope reminds people that, despite their limitations, they have the power to act. When people feel a sense of power, they can move forward and reorient themselves when the barriers appear insurmountable.

Some patients are effective at hoping, while others need help to learn to hope. To support patient hope, clinicians must work for the sake of their patients' overall best interests. Healthcare workers must account for the nonclinical aspects of the patient–provider dynamic.

The fear of false hope is a legitimate concern. In some cases, an attitude of hope may not be the right disposition to adopt, but caution is warranted. If healthcare providers stifle hope based on insufficient information, they infringe upon the sanctity of the patient–provider relationship, a relationship grounded on trust, good will, empathy, and care. Notwithstanding the existence of false hope, the fundamental duty of autonomy supports a patient's right to hope and a provider's obligation not to interfere.

Healthcare providers must not inhibit the right of patients to hope, their right to pursue the good and what they believe is good for them. Clinicians are not obligated to provide treatments that are medically unnecessary and potentially life threatening, but they do have a responsibility to support patients. Patients must be capable of self-governance, but they need the help of their providers when making healthcare decisions.

Hope is both an individual activity and an interpersonal dynamic in the patient–provider relationship. Patients find comfort when they feel that they are not alone and when they have the support of their providers. As hope provides an ability to see the possibility of the good despite the odds, then clinicians must help their patients to interpret and understand information outside an evidence-based framework. Indeed, providers must help their patients to cultivate an ability to see the good, even if the good is not a cure or the avoidance of death but rather the management of suffering. Even if we do not achieve what we want, hope remains good for us. Hope helps us to exercise our values in pursuit of goals, and our values are what define us.

References

Awdish, Rana. *In Shock: My Journey from Death to Recovery and the Redemptive Power of Hope.* New York: Picador, 2017.

Beauchamp, Tom L., and James F. Childress. *Principles of Biomedical Ethics.* 6th ed. New York: Oxford University Press, 2009.

Best, Jennifer. "Instilling Hope and Respecting Patient Autonomy: Reconciling Apparently Conflicting Duties." *Bioethics* 19, no. 3 (2005): 215–231.

Bovens, Luc. "The Value of Hope." *Philosophy and Phenomenological Research* 59 (1999): 667–681.

Frankl, Viktor E. *Man's Search for Meaning.* New York: Beacon Press, 1959.

Groopman, Jerome. *The Anatomy of Hope: How People Prevail in the Face of Illness.* New York: Random House, 2004.

Hernandez, Jill Graper. *Gabriel Marcel's Ethics of Hope: Evil, God and Virtue.* New York: Continuum International Publishing Group, 2011.

Marcel, Gabriel. *Homo Viator: An Introduction to a Metaphysic of Hope.* South Bend, IN: St. Augustine's Press, 2010.

Martin, Adrienne M. *How We Hope: A Moral Psychology.* New Jersey: Princeton University Press, 2014.

McGeer, Victoria. "The Art of Good Hope." *Annals of the American Academy of Political and Social Sciences* 592 (2004): 100–127.

Pettit, Philip. "Hope and Its Place in Mind." *Annals of the American Academy of Political and Social Science* 592 (2004): 152–165.

Sharot, Tali. *The Optimism Bias: A Tour of the Irrationally Positive Brain.* New York: Vintage Books, 2011.

Stratton-Lake, Philip. "Marcel, Hope, and Virtue." In *French Existentialism: Consciousness, Ethics, and Relations with Others.* Edited by James Giles. Atlanta, GA: Rodopi, 1999.

van Hooft, Stan. *Hope.* New York: Routledge, 2011.

Wildes, Kevin. "Hope—A Necessary Virtue for Health Care." *Bioethics Forum* 15, no. 1 (1999): 25–29.

. . . .

Summary

The readings in this unit introduce the complex nature of hope and its relevance in healthcare. While clinicians often fear that hope can metamorphose into something destructive, like false hope, physical therapists should help patients cultivate hope to ensure that patients are acting autonomously. If patients feel powerless, they are unable to sustain their personal identity. Hope equips patients with the power to act and reorients them to better understand their limitations.

The readings also illuminate the deep bond between agency and hope. While the experience of hope can vary from person to person, hope is an inherent fixture in human agency. Hope does not simply happen to us.

Physical therapists take an oath to promote their patients' best interests. However, the fundamental uncertainty in outcomes can affect clinicians' abilities to advocate for their patients' best interests. Clinicians must balance their professional obligations within a climate of doubt.

Hope in the patient encounter is like walking on shaky ground; one must tread carefully to avoid a fall. How hope is cultivated in the clinician–patient relationship is just as important as the advancement of autonomy and maintenance of trust. Hope can be valuable to patient recovery and fuel patients to act in pursuit of their goals. The challenge for providers, however, is knowing when to encourage hope. Clinicians must put themselves in their patient's shoes. If you were Leon, what would you want Steven to tell you? Patients have rights; thus, the choice to hope should not be exclusively dictated by a clinician's concerns and fears.

How a clinician supports a patient matters. Providers are obliged to promote autonomy by helping patients adequately understand their condition. Clinicians must also promote autonomy by helping patients see beyond clinical constraints and instead consider possibility, even if that means adjusting their recovery goals. Providers must find a balance between the clinical facts and the individual needs of each person and, in so doing, foster choice in their patients. When patients fail to achieve their goals, clinicians must refocus, make new plans, and help patients navigate ever-changing and ambiguous circumstances. Hope can strengthen autonomy and help patients regain control in an environment where they have no control. Hope can maintain the authority patients have over their identity. Clinicians ought to support a patient's right to hope but must be careful not to encourage hope for the impossible.

When used correctly, hope can enable both patients and providers to remain themselves, exercise their values, and respect the dignity of relationships. Clinicians must be steadfast in supporting a right to hope because hope enables patients to articulate their values and respects their dignity. The cultivation of hope in the patient–provider relationship becomes a shared activity in pursuit of a common goal of recovery. By investing in hope, patients and clinicians commit to work together and adapt to the healing process.

Comprehension Questions

Hesiod, *Works and Days*

1. Why did Zeus keep fire from humans?
2. What are some of the features that the gods bestowed upon Pandora?
3. After Pandora released the contents of the jar, how was mankind affected?

Nietzsche, *Hope*

1. What phrase does Nietzsche use to describe Pandora's box?
2. How does hope affect humankind?
3. Why does Nietzsche think that hope was the greatest evil in Pandora's box?

Aquinas, *Summa Theologica*

1. What are the four conditions of hope?
2. What makes hope a passion?
3. What makes hope a virtue?
4. Does hope help or hinder action?

van Hooft, *Defining Hope*

1. What are the essential features of hope?
2. What is the difference between hope and wish?
3. Why does van Hooft claim that hope is the activity of hoping?
4. What makes hope a possible virtue?

Johnson, *Hope and Autonomy*

1. What are the positive and negative obligations of the principle of autonomy?
2. What makes hope an additional aspect of respect for autonomy?

3. How does Frankl describe the nature of hope?

4. Why does Frankl think that hope is valuable?

Steven's Story

Developing Your Moral Imagination: Critical Thinking Questions

1. What makes hope valuable?

2. Can you see hope as part of the structure of a person's character and identity?

3. Should clinicians encourage patients to hope?

4. Do you believe that patients have a right to hope?

5. If you were in Leon's situation, how would you want to be helped?

UNIT VI

The Broad Reach of Justice

....

Vern's Story

In the early months of the COVID-19 pandemic, healthcare systems were quickly overwhelmed. Many physical therapists were initially deemed nonessential workers and were consequently furloughed and unable to treat their patients. Imagine Vern, the manager of a physical therapy clinic in a long-term care facility that cares for individuals with physical and intellectual disabilities. When he is able to resume patient care, Vern has limited personal protective equipment for his employees and, given social-distancing restrictions, must significantly limit the number of patients in the clinic. Vern and his staff are committed to their patients and recognize the importance of continuing treatment to maintain and maximize patient function, especially as the patients are fragile and susceptible to decline. Vern must determine how to fairly prioritize and manage care given the pandemic restrictions.

Schema Activation/Response Question
What should Vern think about before making a decision?

Cultivating Professional Values

The APTA core values aim to promote good reasoning. The key values at stake in Vern's story include:

- **Altruism:** sacrificing for others and putting others' needs before your own
- **Collaboration:** working together in pursuit of a shared goal
- **Duty:** fulfilling one's commitment to the profession and meeting the public's trust
- **Integrity:** acting in accord with one's personal and professional moral identity
- **Social Responsibility:** doing good for others and helping the larger community

Introduction to the Topic

All too often in healthcare, matters of justice focus on the fair distribution of goods and services. This unit explores a broader conception of justice and focuses in particular on the meaning of justice as fairness. Taken together, the readings help students not only understand the broad scope of justice but also appreciate the symbiotic relationship among individuals, providers, and their communities. The readings promote critical reflection about the deeper meaning of justice and its consequences.

In Unit I, we explored the basic principles of healthcare ethics—namely, beneficence, nonmaleficence, autonomy, and, in a very general way, justice. These biomedical principles provide an ethical framework for clinicians to evaluate moral conflicts and to protect the rights and interests of individuals. In this unit, we go beyond a notion of procedural justice and focus on the deeper meaning of justice and its broad reach in a socially embedded institution like healthcare.

Classical philosophers like Plato and Aristotle viewed justice as the most essential human virtue because humans are social beings living together in communities. The meaning of justice, though, is bound together with ideals of punishment, revenge, social harmony and unity, fair exchange, and the distribution of goods. Justice is understood in terms of what a person deserves or is owed. Nonetheless, justice remains abstracted from practice and concrete particulars. What is a fair distribution of goods? How should scarce resources be allocated? What do we deserve? Is justice simply a matter of equal treatment, or is justice something bigger?

In his book, *A Theory of Justice*, American political philosopher John Rawls defends his classic conception of justice grounded on egalitarian ideals and liberty.[1] He argues that justice is "the first virtue of social institutions," a view that stresses the importance of liberty and favors equality as central to all social and political arrangements.[2]

Rawls presents his "original position" thought experiment. His hypothetical aims to show how people free from all bias and knowledge of self, others, and society would select principles of justice. Rawls contends that justice must be established by rational beings in an original position behind a veil of ignorance. A person behind this veil does not "know his place in society, his class position or social status; nor does he know his fortune in the distribution of natural assets and abilities."[3]

Rawls states that when people know nothing about themselves and others—and their differences—they will work cooperatively to promote everyone's best interests in even the worst case scenario. Such beings, in an effort to achieve a just social organization, would agree to a conception of justice as fairness: "All social values—liberty and opportunity, income and wealth, and the bases of self-respect—are to be distributed equally unless an unequal distribution of any, or all, of these values is to everyone's advantage."[4] Rawls's thought experiment teaches that we should work together

---

[1] John Rawls, *A Theory of Justice* (Cambridge, MA: Harvard University Press, 1971).

[2] Rawls, *A Theory of Justice*, 3.

[3] Rawls, *A Theory of Justice*, 137.

[4] Rawls, *A Theory of Justice*, 62.

not only in spite of our differences but also with an appreciation of them in order to build a society with equal liberties and equal opportunity.

Rawls argues that social goods must be distributed equally among individuals unless an unequal distribution will be more beneficial. Rawls notes that many of the characteristics that make people different from one another are arbitrarily acquired and should not be used to determine benefits or favors by social institutions. He describes how bias works in our own favor and is manifest in our judgments of others. This bias leads to injustice in the way that goods are distributed. He acknowledges the impact of the natural lottery on social disparities, inequities, and the fulfillment of justice and in so doing affirms two principles of justice as fairness. First, all people share the same basic rights and liberties. Second, all people should have fair equality of opportunity, and focuses on income and wealth. Rawls formulates these principles of justice in order to promote social unity.

Introduction to the Readings

Rawls views justice as tethered to social practices and institutions. However, many of our social systems are based on historical forms of bias related to gender and race. A Rawlsian view of justice as fairness aims to promote impartiality, yet it may fail to fully acknowledge oppressive social arrangements. When the distribution of goods is based on impartial procedures, the distinct needs of individuals may remain unfulfilled.

In the first reading, selections from "The Social Construction of Race," sociologist Steven M. Buechler discusses the nature of race and forms of discrimination. He explains how the concept of race was derived from assumptions about observed differences—notably, phenotypic differences in skin color. Buechler notes that people see "race as a biologically self-evident reality" when it is, in fact, a construction, an artificial imposition created by "a historical process."

Buechler ties his analysis of race to a concept of justice by exploring the discrimination that arises from these false beliefs about the biological origin of race. He explains how discrimination sustains deeply rooted historical beliefs that form the foundation of many of our social systems and conventions. Racial bias leaks into social institutions and results in discrimination in "the economy, employment, and political representation" as well as in "differences in health, mortality, and life expectancy." Phenotypic differences become socially embedded, institutionalized, and judged. Such differences establish a shaky foundation for a conventional sense of justice. Understanding the historical and social construction of race reveals that fair procedures alone cannot create justice.

The second reading, selections from "Healthcare Issues in Contemporary Society," by bioethicist David Lemberg offers concrete examples of the outcomes of bias in healthcare. He defines a health disparity as "a difference in outcomes, or even the existence of an inequality" and health inequity as "unfairness and, possibly, injustice." He offers specific examples of the injustice that occurs in health outcomes and services among various vulnerable and minority populations. He describes different treatment for people of color and the lack of knowledge about the health needs of LGBTQ+ individuals. Healthcare providers often lack knowledge about the specific health needs of various at-risk and vulnerable populations. As a result, individual differences provide fertile ground for discrimination, stigmatization, and victimization. Lemberg acknowledges that many levels of bias operate among healthcare providers, from administrators to clinicians, and that disparities arise as a result of an imbalanced and unfair system.

Lemberg highlights the importance of understanding justice in this context of health disparities and inequities. He describes the social determinants of health, including "early childhood environments; education; housing; economic and work environments; unequal distribution of income, goods, and services; and opportunities for leading a flourishing life." He encourages researchers to educate healthcare workers to recognize bias and to incorporate strategies for including social determinants in patient care. Lemberg illuminates the many difficulties in establishing a just healthcare system.

References

Rawls, John. *A Theory of Justice*. Cambridge, MA: Harvard University Press, 1971.

Selections from "The Social Construction of Race"

By Steven M. Buechler

....

The analysis of social class has been part of sociology from the beginning. Race is different. Although scholars like W. E. B. Du Bois (1903) had crucial insights into race relations more than a hundred years ago, sociology was slow to see race as an important subject in its own right.

This gradually changed after Gunnar Myrdal's *An American Dilemma* (1944) placed racial prejudice at the forefront of public consciousness. Along with other work, it helped establish race and ethnic relations as a major sub field within sociology. Group dynamics, racial conflict, prejudice, and discrimination attracted increasing sociological attention.

What really invigorated the study of race were not academic developments but social conflict. As the civil rights movement overturned the most explicit forms of racial segregation and discrimination in the 1950s and 1960s, race became even more central in public awareness and academic study. As the movement evolved from liberal integration to black power to cultural nationalism, different understandings of race emerged. These movement-inspired analyses revealed how race was embedded in social structure.

Current sociological understandings of race thus have a dual legacy. The slowly developing academic study of race has been infused with critical insights from race-based social movements. [...]

What Is Race?

Few things seem more obvious than someone's race. As we interact with others, we unthinkingly place them within familiar racial categories. On rare occasions, someone doesn't easily fit the categories. We might regard them as odd or unusual, but we rarely use such cases to question the categories themselves.

When we "see" race like this, we are also likely to assume race is rooted in biology. The physical differences between races (skin color, facial features, eye shape, hair texture) seem so self-evident as to be beyond question. Everyday consciousness assumes these features reflect well-established biological, physiological, and genetic differences that distinguish races. Well-meaning people might struggle to avoid prejudices and stereotypes, but they are likely to see race as a biologically self-evident reality.

This is a good time to recall Peter Berger's (1963) sociological insight that things are not always what they seem. Beneath the seemingly self-evident biology of race, there are complex social, political, and cultural forces that sustain that appearance. Put differently, race is not biologically determined but rather socially constructed. This implies two seemingly contradictory things. First, racial categories are arbitrary. They have little scientific or biological foundation. They are not "real." Second, these categories nevertheless *become real* through social definitions. As W. I. Thomas noted long ago, if a situation is defined as real, it will be real in its consequences. When the definition is embedded in centuries of institutions and interactions, then race becomes as real as any social phenomenon can be. Race is an illusory biological fiction but a powerful social fact.

There are several reasons to question the biological basis of race. Human beings share almost 99 percent of our genetic composition with higher primates. Put differently, homo sapiens are only 1 to 2 percent genetically different from chimpanzees. If the genetic margin separating two species is so small, the likelihood that there will be consistent genetic differences *within* the category of homo sapiens that sort humans into genetically distinct races is highly implausible.

A second reason to doubt the biological basis of race involves the logic of categories and classification. Such logic makes sense when things fall into mutually exclusive categories based on many relevant traits. It makes less sense if there is a lot of overlap between things in supposedly separate categories. The logic is weakest when there is more individual variation within categories than the average variation between categories. And yet it is this weakest version that applies to race. On any number of physical traits, individual variations within races far exceed average differences between them. When categories persist in such situations, it is because they are based on social definitions rather than on logically compelling reasons or scientifically verifiable data.

A third reason to doubt the biological basis of race involves the history of racial typologies. Systems of racial classification have been proposed for centuries, with none of the logical consistency, cumulative advances, or increasing specificity that define scientific progress. Throughout this history, there has been major disagreement over things as basic as how many races exist. After centuries of work, the only real lesson here is that the very idea of distinguishing races in biological terms is not scientifically feasible.

A fourth reason to question the biological basis of race involves social and legal definitions. When Southern legislators defined people as "Negro" if one thirty-second of their ancestry was African, this was a social definition and not a biological fact. When Native American tribes use similar measures to determine who is a legitimate tribal member, this is also a social definition and not a biological fact. Because racial definitions vary by place, you can change your race by flying to Brazil where an unusually complex set of racial distinctions will define your race differently from the place you just left (Henslin 2005, 327). Racial definitions also change over time; consider "how the Irish became white" (Ignatiev 1995) in nineteenth-century US history.

One final example: People sometimes defend a biological conception of race based on medical conditions. In the United States, sickle-cell anemia is considered a "black disease." In reality, a predisposition to sickle-cell anemia derives front geography and evolution and not race. In places where malaria was a big threat to human health, a few people had a natural immunity. Through natural selection, they reproduced in greater numbers. However, the same factors creating the immunity also made them susceptible to sickle-cell anemia. Thus, some but not all Africans are susceptible, and some non-Africans from Mediterranean regions and South Asia are susceptible. It is difficult to see how this qualifies as a "racial" disease (Adelman 2003).

It is not physical but social facts that make races "real." This social construction of race is a historical process. People have always noted human differences, but a new discourse of race emerged during European exploration, conquest, and colonization typically dated from the "discovery" of the "New World" in 1492. Thus, Columbus's diaries refer to the "savages" he encountered. With each subsequent encounter between European colonizers and indigenous groups, the discourse of race grew to describe these "others" in racial terms (Winant 2004).

This discourse rested on two premises. The first was that races were biological realities. The second was that races existed in a hierarchy of superiority and inferiority. In these hierarchies, whites, Europeans, or some subgroup of Europeans were inevitably located at the top of the hierarchy. Despite many variations, some races (the people doing the classifying) were always superior to others (the people being classified). The very concept of race is *racist,* because beliefs about superiority and inferiority have always been part of the concept.

The reasons are not a big mystery. European colonization was often brutal and inhumane. It contradicted many social norms, religious principles, and moral imperatives of the colonizers. It required some type of legitimation of the contradiction between humane values and inhumane behavior. Thus the invention of race/racism.

Colonialism only poses a moral dilemma if people are seen as equals. The social construction of race/racism defines the colonized group as inferior or subhuman. The more their humanity is denied, the more brutality becomes acceptable. Consider that few people have qualms about the slaughter and consumption of animals because they are seen as a different species. It hardly occurs to us that this requires a justification. Some versions of racism also suggest that "others" are a different species, so the moral code of the dominant group does not apply. The same logic operates in warfare; it is easier to kill people who are seen as less than human. It is no accident that the most extreme versions of racial thinking culminate in genocide, where others are not only seen as subhuman but as a threat that must be eliminated.

The social construction of race links biology, inferiority, and racism in fateful ways. Like race, racism has many variations. It can provide justifications for enslavement and genocide. It can seek to convert others who have not yet had the benefits of "civilization." It can portray "others" as innocent children requiring protection and guidance. In every version, however, a presumption of racial inferiority is central.

The social construction of race and racism was vital in legitimizing European colonization and conquest. The United States followed suit in the exploitation of African slaves, the conquest of Native peoples, and racist relations with Latino/a and Asian populations. The timing and groups were different, but the history of US race relations mirrors the European model quite closely.

Although race is a biological fiction, there is a social logic to why this fiction arose and how it shapes contemporary society. The challenge of seeing race as a social construction is to balance the seeming contradiction that something arbitrary has been socially constructed into something as "real" as any social fact can be. [...]

Forms of Discrimination

The colonial model offers a big picture of race relations that rests on many small episodes of discrimination. It is these practices, enacted on a daily basis, that sustain the social construction of race.

Discrimination ranges across many institutions and social arenas. It obviously includes the economy, employment, and political representation. It also includes differences in health, mortality, and life expectancy as a result of differential access to physical and mental health services. It includes deeply rooted patterns of residential segregation that create other problems like unequal access to education. It includes very different probabilities of becoming caught up in the criminal justice system. The effects of discrimination are cumulative, as initial disadvantages become larger inequities over time. Acts of discrimination are the building blocks of racial inequality.

The traditional view of discrimination is that prejudicial attitudes cause discriminatory behavior (Feagin and Feagin 1978). The term *prejudice* means to "prejudge" people on the basis of their group identity. Such judgments often involve negative stereotypes about an entire category of people that are attributed to all its members.

The discrimination that results from prejudice can be explicit, as when people engage in name-calling, racist behavior, or hate crimes. But it can also be subtle or covert. If someone is advertising a job or an apartment and the "wrong" applicant appears, that applicant might be told that the job has been filled or the apartment rented. When the "right" applicant comes along, the apartment or job suddenly becomes available again. In this case, intentional harm is done to someone who might not be aware that they have been the victim of discrimination. Explicit discrimination grabs headlines, but subtle, covert forms are more common and often go undetected. Indeed, it is impossible to know the full extent of discrimination, because much of it is hidden in this fashion. The common thread is a prejudicial attitude. In the traditional model, discrimination occurs when "evil motives" are translated into action.

This model implies that reducing prejudice reduces discrimination. This was part of the logic behind social policies and court decisions favoring integration. It was thought that, with more social contact between groups, people would rethink their prejudices and treat others as individuals and not stereotypes. If prejudice melted away, discrimination would, too. Although the logic seems plausible, there's a problem. By many measures, prejudice in the United States has declined, but racial discrimination has not shown a corresponding reduction.

This prompted a closer look at the traditional view. It became clear that prejudice alone might not lead to discrimination. Prejudiced people need the power to act on prejudice if it is to become discrimination. It also became more evident that discrimination can occur without prejudice. Thus, an employer might have no prejudice against certain people but still refuse to hire them out of a belief that it would drive customers away.

More generally, discrimination limits opportunities for "others" and increases them for discriminators. In such cases, discrimination simply flows from group interest without prejudice. Such discrimination without an "evil motive" can also be an unintentional by-product of institutional policies. As the limits of the traditional model became more evident, sociologists developed another way of thinking about what causes discrimination.

The result was the institutional model in which organizational practices replace prejudice as the major cause of discrimination (Feagin and Feagin 1978). The idea is that social institutions routinely discriminate against many people. In contrast to the traditional model, the institutional model sees discrimination as a normal, routine, chronic outcome rather than a sporadic one. It recognizes that most discrimination is subtle or covert, although overt institutional discrimination still happens, too. It sees discrimination as something that affects thousands if not millions of people, because it is embedded in major social institutions like the criminal justice system or the labor market. Finally, institutional discrimination can be either intentional or unintentional.

Intentional institutional discrimination occurs when there is a conscious goal of unequal treatment. It might be rooted in prejudice, racism, group interest, or some other motive. As with the traditional model, there is an "evil motive" behind such action. Unlike the traditional model, it is not individuals but large organizations that enact these behaviors. In systems of apartheid or legalized segregation, discriminatory purposes are officially proclaimed.

When segregation becomes illegal, intentions to discriminate might no longer be publicly stated but can continue to shape institutional functioning. The redlining of certain neighborhoods as poor credit risks is one example. The use of racial profiling in police practices is another example. The purging of voter registration lists is a third example of intentional, institutional discrimination (Moore 2001). While rarer hate crimes grab headlines, more routine institutional discrimination affects many more people on a daily basis.

Institutional discrimination can also be unintentional. This is indicated by effects rather than motives. Here, we must work backward from discriminatory outcomes to identify the practice or policy that produced them. An example is "side-effect" discrimination that occurs as an unintended by-product of some other practice. Imagine a university that uses an entrance exam to screen applicants. Assume the exam contains no subtle racial biases. Nonetheless, if applicants have been unequally prepared by previous schooling to perform well on this exam, it will produce discriminatory outcomes despite the best of intentions.

A related example is "past-in-present" discrimination where a current practice unwittingly perpetuates prior discrimination. Consider a layoff policy based on seniority. This is not discriminatory in itself. But to whatever extent racial minorities or women have shorter or more episodic work histories as a result of past discrimination, implementing layoffs by seniority will benefit white males and harm minorities and women despite good intentions.

Unintentional discrimination harms many but remains elusive, because it cannot be traced back to a specific person or group with evil motives. In a final twist, it is also possible for "sophisticated racists" who *do* have evil motives to use practices that do not *appear* to intentionally discriminate, knowing that such practices are difficult to identify (Feagin and Feagin 1978).

According to the traditional model, reducing discrimination requires reducing prejudice. According to the institutional model, reducing discrimination requires changing institutions. Whereas the traditional model is "optimistic" that increased social contact will reduce prejudice and discrimination, the institutional model is "pessimistic" that institutions will not simply evolve into less discriminatory behavior. Indeed, the institutional model suggests that if nothing is done, discrimination will continue indefinitely, because institutions are self-perpetuating and because some groups benefit from discriminatory practices.

This is the logic behind affirmative action. It assumes that discrimination will continue unless affirmative action is taken to change the practices that produce it. As a policy, most affirmative action programs involve voluntary efforts to increase the diversity of a pool of qualified applicants. Such policies target informal practices whereby people tend to recruit, hire, or admit people like themselves. By creating policies that require looking beyond familiar social circles when recruiting applicants, affirmative action programs have made modest contributions to reducing discriminatory outcomes.

The persistence of racial inequality in the United States has also prompted a rethinking of the traditional focus on individual prejudice. New research has led one analyst to conclude that in the post—civil rights era, we have entered a time of "racism without racists" (Bonilla-Silva 2003). This argument downplays prejudicial attitudes by suggesting that racism rests on a material foundation of group interests and white privilege. Racism persists because whites derive substantial material benefits from it. Thus, even when whites do not have stereotypical views of minorities, they often perpetuate racism in ways that obscure its victims and beneficiaries.

Where traditional prejudice often assumed biological differences, "color-blind racism" is a more complex racial ideology emphasizing cultural differences. Four distinct frames express color-blind racism (Bonilla-Silva 2003). "Abstract liberalism" uses familiar political discourse about individual rights and equal opportunity to subtly deny structural barriers and implicitly blame victims. "Naturalism" suggests that segregation reflects freely chosen preferences of people to associate with others like them. "Cultural racism" identifies supposedly defective values, beliefs, and practices within minority cultures that are responsible for their lack of progress. Finally, "minimizing racism" acknowledges lingering problems of discrimination while emphasizing how much progress has been made. The implication is that such problems no longer require systemic solutions.

None of these frames sound overtly racist. Indeed, they sound quite reasonable by comparison. They still function, however, as an ideology legitimizing racial inequality. Color-blind racism denies or minimizes institutional barriers and uses the rhetoric of individual opportunity and cultural differences to blame minorities and excuse whites for racial inequality. The emergence of "racism without racists" illustrates how racial meanings and definitions change over time. To analyze such changes, we need to revisit the idea that race is socially constructed.

Racial Formation

The theory of racial formation sees the social construction of race as a contested process of ongoing conflict (Omi and Winant 1994; Winant 1994, 2004). "[R]ace can be defined as a *concept that signifies and symbolizes socio-political conflicts and interests in reference to different types of human bodies*" (Winant 2004, 155; italics in original). The theory of racial formation also insists on the "reality" of race despite its origins as a social construction.

The challenge is to understand the simultaneous "arbitrariness" and "reality" of race. It arises once race is decoupled from biology. This has often led social scientists to reduce race to some other kind of group and transpose their experiences onto races. This problematic response implies that if race is not about biology, then it is not about anything real. The theory of racial formation maintains that race is not about biology, but it *is* still about something very real. That reality, moreover, needs to be understood on its own terms and not reduced to something else.

One way mainstream perspectives have denied the reality of race is by equating it with ethnicity and using the ethnicity paradigm to analyze race relations. This inevitably turns the discussion back to assimilation. Despite the different histories of racial minorities and white ethnics in the United States, some maintain that racial minorities will eventually undergo the same assimilation as white ethnic groups in earlier decades and centuries. Rather than analyzing race on its own terms, this substitutes the history of ethnic assimilation as a goal for race relations.

This reduction of race to ethnicity is problematic, because it denies the unique features of racial formation (Omi and Winant 1994). It falsely transposes white experience onto nonwhites. It denies ethnic variations within racial groups by equating broad racial categories ("African American") with specific white ethnicities ("Italian"). The ethnicity paradigm also advocates individualistic solutions like upward mobility. The reduction of race to ethnicity thus obscures the distinctiveness of racial oppression and proposes unachievable or undesirable solutions to racial conflict.

An alternative is the class paradigm. This approach reduces race to class or sees the real meaning of race through a class lens. The class paradigm underscores how members of racial minorities are disproportionately located in the working class or lower socioeconomic levels. The logic is that their fates are determined more by their class position than by their racial identity. Moreover, race has been used to reinforce class exploitation when employers designate racial minorities as a secondary labor force, divide workers along racial lines, and play one group off the other to the detriment of both. In this paradigm, race is important for its role in a more fundamental set of class dynamics.

Although it illuminates intersections of race and class, this paradigm is not sufficient for understanding racial formation on its own terms. It simply assumes class is fundamental and race is secondary. Moreover, the equation of racial minorities with only one class oversimplifies race and implies that middle- or upper-class minorities face no racial barriers. "It would be more accurate to say that race and class are competing modalities by which social actors may be organized" (Omi and Winant 1994, 32). If so, the class model with its reduction of race to class is insufficient.

A third alternative is the nation paradigm or the internal colonialism model discussed earlier. As we saw, this model emphasizes differences between the assimilationist history of white ethnic groups and the quasi-colonial status of racial minorities. The metaphor of colonial relations has much to tell us about the history of race relations within the United States. As a viable model of contemporary racial formation, however, it has serious limitations.

In a postcolonial world of global mobility, equating races with geographically bounded nations is an increasingly implausible way to think about race relations. There is substantially more interracial contact in contemporary, racially diverse societies than in classic colonial relations. The nation paradigm also obscures increasingly important class differences among minorities by reducing them to a homogeneous, cultural nationality. Although more instructive than the ethnicity and class paradigms, this one also falls short as a way to understand racial formation.

The problem is that each paradigm—ethnicity, class, and nation—reduces race to something else. Each fails to see race on its own terms. The solution is to move beyond these paradigms to a model that sees race as an independently constructed social reality.

This means seeing racial formation as a process in which social, economic, and political forces determine the meaning of racial categories in a given historical context. To emphasize the importance of process, the term *racialization* is coined (Omi and Winant 1994) to refer to the extension of racial meanings to relationships that were previously not classified in such terms.

Consider slavery. Although US planters used African Americans as slave labor for centuries, the practice did not originate for racial reasons. It derived from the economic realities of plantation agriculture. In order to be profitable, such agriculture requires the cheapest possible labor. Planters first used white indentured servants from Europe and then captured Native Americans (Geschwender 1978). Neither group worked out well in the long run. Importing African slave labor gradually emerged as a later alternative in the search for cheap labor. Once the practice was institutionalized, slavery was racialized through racist beliefs and legitimations to justify the use of black slave labor by white, "God-fearing" Christians. Slavery became racialized over time. In other words, "we know that racism did not create slavery, but that slavery created racism" (Winant 2004, 84).

Institutions, practices, and beliefs become "raced" when they are shaped and understood through racial categories. Consider how many urban social problems have become "raced," as popular consciousness and media representations link race with poverty, welfare, gangs, drugs, and crime. These issues involve many more whites than nonwhites, but their racialized nature becomes a self-fulfilling prophecy. Thus, people act on racialized beliefs about crime and who commits it, leading to highly disproportionate numbers of racial minorities being suspected, arrested, convicted, and incarcerated for "raced" definitions of crime. The differential penalties for crack cocaine used by minorities and powder cocaine favored by whites is one of the more blatant examples of such racialization.

The most important raced institution is the state. In a racially divided society, the state racializes many social dynamics. "For most of U.S. history, the states main objective in its racial policy was repression and exclusion" (Omi and Winant 1994, 81). It commenced with the Naturalization Act of 1790 that limited citizenship to free, white immigrants. The pattern continued throughout the nineteenth century as racialized policies of repression and exclusion regulated race relations. A more recent example of state power is the creation of the category "Hispanic" in 1980, racializing a new group of people and embedding the category in state policies, practices, and institutions. States and racial formation are thus closely intertwined.

Racial formation is not just about top-down power. When a collective identity is constructed and used to dominate people, that same identity will eventually become a rallying point for resistance. Whether the identity involves race, ethnicity, gender, nationality, or sexuality, domination provokes resistance. Thus, racial formation is a contested process. People fight back, and even powerful elites cannot completely control racial formation for long. It is more accurate to see racial formation—and the social construction of race more generally—as an ongoing struggle over what race means. Authorities use race to subordinate groups, and racially defined groups use it to resist subordination.

The contested quality of racial formation is evident in recent racial politics. On the eve of the civil rights movement of the 1950s and 1960s, racial formation took the form of domination. White power was the norm, backed up by coercion, segregation, exclusion, and violence. In this period, racial formation was a top-down affair, because of the overwhelming power of whites. Collective resistance appeared futile.

Social changes nevertheless created opportunities to contest racial formation. The disruptions of World War II, the partial integration of the armed forces, the mechanization of Southern agriculture, and migration from the rural South to the urban North all undermined racial domination. When the civil rights movement appeared in the 1950s, it echoed the ethnicity paradigm with themes of individualism, opportunity, and integration. That such a modest agenda provoked such a ferocious backlash is revealing. Simply asking for what whites took for granted amounted to an almost revolutionary challenge to racial domination.

The movement soon transcended the ethnicity paradigm, in part because of the resistance it encountered to its integrationist goals. But the shift was also sparked by "the rearticulation of black collective subjectivity" (Omi and Winant 1994, 98). In other words, black activists made the redefinition of racial identity a central goal. The movement *made* racial formation a two-way street by challenging static notions of race and racial hierarchy. In effect, activists reclaimed the meaning of race from a white power structure and made it their own.

These events transformed the civil rights movement. Activists adopted multiple racial paradigms and diverse political strategies. "Entrists" argued that strategic participation in elections and mainstream institutions could transform the state. Socialists tried to build class alliances across racial lines and link struggles against racism and capitalism. Nationalists encouraged a separatist response of institution building and cultural pride within minority communities. None met with complete success. The entrist, socialist, and nationalist strategies had the same shortcomings as the ethnicity, class, and nation paradigms on which they were based. Each reduced race to something else and missed the complexity of racial formation. This activism nevertheless shattered older understandings of race and put racial formation center stage (Omi and Winant 1994).

As the movement became more complex, so did the response of the raced state. In some instances, it brutally repressed militant leaders and groups that challenged its authority. More broadly, the state shifted from racial domination to racial hegemony. This meant incorporating oppositional challenges in ways that defused their transformative potential. "Under hegemonic conditions, opposition and difference are not repressed, excluded, or silenced (at least not primarily). Rather, they are inserted, often after suitable modification, within a 'modern' (or perhaps 'postmodern') social order" (Winant 1994, 29). Although hegemony might be less violent than outright domination, it amounts to a more complex system of racial control.

Racial hegemony has sparked competing racial projects on both sides. On the reactionary side, the far right still equates race with biology and advocates violence to prevent all forms of "race mixing." The new right translates old-fashioned racism into code words that are not explicitly racist but nonetheless trigger racist attitudes and actions among those who know the code. The neoconservative right uses egalitarian language to advocate individualism and reject group-oriented solutions. They use the rhetoric of a color-blind society while ignoring the historical legacy of being a color-conscious society. This is the most sophisticated defense of the white power structure. It uses familiar, liberal ideas to argue for illiberal ends. It exemplifies "racism without racists" advocating "color-blind racism" (Bonilla-Silva 2003).

On the progressive side, pragmatic liberalism appeals to group identities to mobilize political support for racially progressive policies, including affirmative action. It advocates pluralism and tolerance and attempts a difficult balancing act between advancing minority rights and maintaining social peace. Finally, radical democrats seek full acceptance of racial difference and identities in the name of autonomy. They seek democratization of the state and redistributive policies to foster racial equality (Winant 1994).

Racial formation is thus a dynamic, contested set of social and political meanings. The current diversity of racial politics—consisting of at least five distinct and competing racial projects—testifies to the fluidity of racial formation and the social construction of race.

The Construction of Whiteness

It is intriguing that whites attribute "race" to "people of color" but don't see "white" as a "color." It's as if race applies to people who differ from the norm but not the group that is the norm. Given this, it is important to turn the microscope back on the dominant group and its construction of whiteness.

Like other socially constructed racial categories, whiteness emerged historically. Consider how "the Irish became white" over decades of conflict and eventual assimilation in the United States. More pointedly, this is the story of "how the Catholic Irish, an oppressed race in Ireland, became part of an oppressing race in America" (Ignatiev 1995, 1). When Irish immigrants first arrived in the United States, they were perceived as an inferior race by Anglo-Saxon powers on both sides of the Atlantic. However, rather than joining with other subordinate races, the Irish distanced themselves from minorities and aligned with whites. They pursued the classic assimilationist trade-off: "In becoming white the Irish ceased to be Green" (Ignatiev 1995, 3). This suggests that assimilation means moving toward the dominant group and away from minorities, because the dominant group is defined precisely by its distance from racial minorities. Until a group made both moves, assimilation was unlikely.

The Irish example fits a broader template of how whiteness was created through an amalgamation of initially diverse ethnicities. This history falls into three periods (Jacobson 1998, 13–14). From the founding of the country into the mid-nineteenth century, citizenship was confined to "free white" immigrants, implicitly meaning Anglo-Saxon and sometimes other Northern European peoples. From the mid-nineteenth century to the early twentieth century, immigration from Southern, Central, and Eastern Europe challenged the equation of whiteness and Northern European descent. During this period, a complex racial politics initially defined these immigrants as inferior races at the same time that they sought a broadening of the definition of "white" to include them. It has only been since the 1920s that ethnic differences were downplayed and a more generic white identity was forged. This period "redrew the dominant racial configuration along the strict, binary line of white and black, creating Caucasians where before had been so many Celts, Hebrews, Teutons, Mediterraneans, and Slavs" (Jacobson 1998, 14).

By the mid-twentieth century, whiteness became the dominant racial norm. This proved short-lived, as "it is no longer possible to assume a 'normalized' whiteness, whose invisibility and relatively monolithic character signify immunity from political or cultural challenge" (Winant 2004, 50). As race-based social movements recast their own racial subjectivity, white identity also became more self-conscious.

As white dominance was challenged, it triggered "grievances of the privileged." Some whites claimed they were under attack "simply for their race." Others decried a world in which minorities seemed to get advantages withheld from whites through "reverse discrimination." Still other whites lamented the lack of a distinct and vivid white culture they could identify with just as other races identified with theirs. Such defensive responses imply that although whites are still dominant, such dominance can no longer be taken for granted.

These responses also belie the ongoing privileges of the dominant group. White privilege means that despite recent challenges to the racial order, it continues to be organized in ways that benefit the dominant group. Such privilege is often invisible to those who benefit, while being highly visible to those who pay the price.

This is nicely captured in Peggy McIntosh's (2005) efforts to teach about male privilege in women's studies courses. Her female students quickly grasped the concept and readily supplied examples. Her male students conceded that women faced certain disadvantages but denied their male privilege. To understand this denial, McIntosh examined her own dual status as a white woman. As a woman, she could readily see male privilege. As a white, she had difficulty seeing her racial privilege, just as men had difficulty seeing male privilege. The broader pattern is that privileged groups rarely recognize their own privileges and perceive any challenge to them as victimization. Such complaints are not simply disingenuous; they reflect a real inability to see how whiteness and maleness continue conferring privileges even in a social order undergoing challenge and reformulation.

These privileges come in two categories. "Unearned advantages" are "positive" privileges that should not be abolished but made available to all. The privilege of not being a crime suspect simply on the basis of one's race is an unearned advantage for whites that should ideally be an unearned entitlement for all. "Conferred dominance" involves "negative" privileges that need to be abolished to create racial equality. Discrimination that benefits dominant groups at the expense of subordinate ones fits this type; it should be abolished in any society seeking racial equality (McIntosh 2005).

These are now the goals of a "new abolitionist racial project." Proponents of this movement identify white privilege as the lynchpin of white supremacy and see rejection of privilege by whites as essential to creating a just racial order. Advocates put a positive spin on the epithet "race traitor" by countering that "treason to whiteness is loyalty to humanity" (Winant 2004, 63). As this racial project unfolds alongside others described earlier, it is difficult to deny that we are in a period of highly contested racial formation.

Understanding race requires looking beyond taken-for-granted appearances. It also requires a multilayered analysis of domination. Critical sociology is tailor-made for both tasks. It illuminates both the social construction of race and the challenges seeking to deconstruct racial hierarchies in the name of a more egalitarian society.

References

Adelman, Larry. 2003. *Race: The Power of an Illusion.* Videodisc, California Newsreel.

Berger, Peter. 1963. *Invitation to Sociology.* Doubleday.

Bonilla-Silva, Eduardo. 2003. *Racism without Racists.* Rowman & Littlefield.

Du Bois, W. E. B. 1903/1989. *The Souls of Black Folk.* Bantam Books.

Feagin, Joe, and Clairece Booher Feagin. 1978. *Discrimination American Style.* Prentice Hall.

Geschwender, James. 1978. *Racial Stratification in America.* Wm. C. Brown.

Henslin, James. 2005. *Sociology.* 7th ed. Allyn and Bacon.

Ignatiev, Noel. 1995. *How the Irish Became White.* Routledge.

Jacobson, Matthew. 1998. *Whiteness of a Different Color.* Harvard University Press.

McIntosh, Peggy. 2005. "White Privilege and Male Privilege." In *Great Divides,* ed. Thomas Shapiro, 300–307. McGraw-Hill.

Moore, Michael. 2001. *Stupid White Men.* Regan.

Myrdal, Gunnar. 1944. *An American Dilemma.* Harper and Row.

Omi, Michael, and Howard Winant. 1994. *Racial Formation in the United States.* 2nd ed. Routledge.

Winant, Howard. 1994. *Racial Conditions.* University of Minnesota Press.

———. 2004. *The New Politics of Race.* University of Minnesota Press.

Selection from "Healthcare Issues in Contemporary Society"

By David Lemberg

....

[...]

Health Disparities/Health Inequities

In addition to biomedical research, healthcare policy and advocacy is an arena for ethical investigation and assessment. [...] the National Institutes of Health defines health disparities as "gaps in the quality of health and health care that mirror differences in socioeconomic status, racial and ethnic background, and education level."[1] *Healthy People 2020* defines health disparities as

> a particular type of health difference that is closely linked with social, economic, and/or environmental disadvantage. Health disparities adversely affect groups of people who have systematically experienced greater obstacles to health based on their racial or ethnic group; religion; socioeconomic status; gender; age; mental health; cognitive, sensory, or physical disability; sexual orientation or gender identity; geographic location; or other characteristics historically linked to discrimination or exclusion.[2]

The term "health disparity" was coined in the United States around 1990[3] and represents differences among socioeconomic groups in the areas of availability, access, and quality of healthcare;

---

[1] National Institute of Allergy and Infectious Diseases, *Minority Health*, https://www.niaid.nih.gov/research/minority-health.

[2] HealthyPeople.gov, *Healthy People 2020, Disparities*, https://www.healthypeople.gov/2020/about/foundation-health-measures/Disparities.

[3] P. Braveman, "What Are Health Disparities and Health Equity? We Need to Be Clear," *Public Health Reports* 129, suppl. 2 (2014): 5–8.

health status; and health outcomes.[4] In efforts to improve health and reduce the incidence and prevalence of disease, the global scientific community has conducted extensive research and translated research into evidence-based guides for public health practice.[5] In the United States, these guides include *The Guide to Community Preventive Services*[6] and the Institute of Medicine's *Unequal Treatment: Confronting Racial and Ethnic Disparities in Health Care.*[7] An international example is the World Health Organization's *Action Plan for the Global Strategy for the Prevention and Control of Noncommunicable Diseases.*[8]

But health disparities persist, in the United States and around the world, indicating the complex and multifactorial basis of their origins. For example, in the United States, from 2011 through 2014, the age-adjusted percentage of all men and women over age twenty with hypertension was 30.4. In contrast, the comparable rate for non-Hispanic black men was 42.4 percent and the comparable rate for non-Hispanic black women was 44.0 percent.[9] From 2011 through 2014, the percentage of all children and adolescents aged two to nineteen with obesity was 17.0 percent. The comparable rate for Hispanic or Latino children and adolescents in the same age group was 21.9 percent, with the comparable rate for non-Hispanic black or African American children and adolescents being 19.5 percent.[10] Obesity has been defined as a body mass index at or above the sex- and age-specific 95th percentile of the Centers for Disease Control growth charts.[11] Regarding infant mortality, the rate in the U.S. decreased from 7.04 infant deaths per 1,000 live births in 1999 to 5.96 in 2013. However, for non-Hispanic black mothers, the infant mortality rate was 11.11 in 2013. For American Indians or Alaska Natives, the infant mortality rate was 7.72 in 2013.[12] From 1980 through 2014, for both males and females, life expectancy at birth in the United States was longest for white persons and shortest for black persons. In 2014, life expectancy at birth was 76.5 years for non-Hispanic white males and 72.0 years for non-Hispanic black males. In 2014, life expectancy at birth was 81.1 years for non-Hispanic white females and 78.1 years for non-Hispanic black females.[13] Importantly, most

[4] O. Carter-Pokras and C. Baquet, "What Is a "Health Disparity," *Public Health Reports* 117, no. 5 (2002): 426–434.

[5] H. K. Koh, S. C. Oppenheimer, S. B. Massin-Short et al., "Translating Research Evidence into Practice to Reduce Health Disparities: A Social Determinants Approach," *American Journal of Public Health* 100, suppl. 1 (2010): S72–S80.

[6] Task Force on Community Preventive Services, *The Guide to Community Preventive Services: What Works to Promote Health?*, eds. S. Zaza. P. A. Briss, and K. W. Harris (New York: Oxford University Press, 2005).

[7] B. D. Smedley, A. Y. Stith, and A. R. Nelson, eds., *Unequal Treatment: Confronting Racial and Ethnic Disparities in Health Care* (Washington, DC: National Academies Press, 2003).

[8] World Health Organization (WHO), *2008–2013 Action Plan for the Global Strategy for the Prevention and Control of Noncommunicable Diseases* (Geneva: WHO, 2008), http://www.who.int/nmh/publications/9789241597418/en/.

[9] Centers for Disease Control and Prevention, National Center for Health Statistics: Health, United States, 2015, with Special Feature on Racial and Ethnic Health Disparities. DHHS Publication No. 2016-1232. Washington, D.C., Department of Health and Human Services, 2016, pp. 43 and 61—https://www.cdc.gov/nchs/data/hus/hus15.pdf.

[10] Ibid., 26, 43.

[11] Centers for Disease Control and Prevention, *Clinical Growth Charts*, https://www.cdc.gov/growthcharts/clinical_charts.htm.

[12] Centers for Disease Control and Prevention, *Health, United States, 2015*, 23, 39.

[13] Ibid., 22.

Americans across all ethnic and racial groups continue to be unaware of the existence of health disparities in any context.[14]

In order to sharpen the focus and improve the outcomes of public policy initiatives directed toward redressing these issues, it is useful to identify the differences among the terms *disparity, inequality,* and *inequity.* Disparity is defined as (1) difference, dissimilarity, incongruity, or an instance of this and (2) inequality or an instance of inequality.[15] Inequality is defined as a lack of equality among persons or things; superiority or inferiority as related to some condition; and "inconsistency of people or distribution of things; unfairness; inequity."[16] Inequity is defined as "lack of equity of justice; unfairness."[17] Thus, recognition of a *health disparity* represents acknowledgment of the existence of a difference in outcomes, or even the existence of an inequality. In contrast, recognition of a health inequity represents acknowledgment of unfairness and, possibly, injustice. Health inequities are "differences in health which are not only unnecessary and avoidable but, in addition, are considered unfair and unjust."[18] Although disparity may be defined as inequality and inequality may be defined as inequity, the term *health inequity* directly emphasizes the condition of lack of equity or lack of justice, with the implicit requirement or need to rectify such injustice. Importantly, what is unequal is not necessarily unjust or inequitable. Public policy development and implementation, as well as civic and community participation and follow-through, may be more comprehensive, consistent, and effective when the policies are directed toward issues of health inequities rather than those of health disparities. For example, public policy in the United Kingdom declares that all health differences between worse-off and better-off socioeconomic groups represent health inequities.[19]

As noted, health inequities among racial, ethnic, and socioeconomic groups persist despite decades of research and numerous public policy initiatives. These injustices may begin to be addressed by implementing a social determinants approach and emphasizing translation of research efficacy into community effectiveness.[20] Most often, public policy begins with a focus on improving access to and affordability of healthcare services, as with the Patient Protection and Affordable Care Act (ACA) of 2010.[21] However, regarding redress of health inequities, availability of healthcare is not sufficient, as its

---

[14] Institute of Medicine, How *Far Have We Come in Reducing Health Disparities? Progress Since 2000. Workshop Summary,* ed. K. M. Anderson (Washington, DC: National Academies Press, 2012), https://www.nap.edu/catalog/13383/how-far-have-we-come-in-reducing-health-disparities-progress.

[15] Brown, *New Shorter Oxford English Dictionary on Historical Principles,* 697.

[16] Ibid., 1357.

[17] Ibid.

[18] M. Whitehead, "The Concepts and Principles of Equity and Health," *Health Promotion International* 6, no. 3 (1991): 217–228.

[19] PAHO/WHO, Division of Health and Human Development, *Principles and Basic Concepts of Equity and Health. 1999,* http://www1.paho.org/english/hdp/hdd/pahowho.pdf.

[20] Koh et al., "Translating Research Evidence into Practice," S74.

[21] Patient Protection and Affordable Care Act (Public Law 111-148, March 23, 2010), https://www.gpo.gov/fdsys/pkg/PLAW-111publ148/pdf/PLAW-111publ148.pdf.

effects are likely to be constrained "relative to the impacts of social and physical environments."[22] These social determinants of health include early childhood environments; education; housing; economic and work environments;[23] unequal distribution of income, goods, and services; and opportunities of leading a flourishing life.[24]

Thus, improving the health and well-being of individuals, families, and communities depends not only on the provision of healthcare services, but also on enhanced understanding of the complexity of interactions represented by the social determinants of health and implementation of actions directed toward creating more equitable conditions and circumstances of life. Problematically, there is a lack of ability to clearly identify the specific social determinants of health that are associated with a particular inequality and to quantify the magnitude of those determinants.[25] Limitations to formulating effective public policies include the following:

- Lack of specific knowledge regarding how to avoid a disparity
- Which social determinants of health are susceptible to intervention
- How to implement changes based on what is known

One way forward focuses on extensive evidence of fundamental and pervasive links between education and income levels and access to resources and opportunities that shape and determine health.[26] Substantial progress toward redressing health inequities may likely be obtained via the determinants of income and education.

Development of robust public policies that will effectively reduce and eliminate health disparities and health inequities is ideally based on wide-ranging social sciences and medical research. An integrated approach includes health assessments, social and economic factors, the physical environment including housing and land use, community support networks, and access to health services. Health disparities may be assessed in the overlapping contexts of population, geography, disease, and risk factors.[27] Overall, research is required that not only uncovers potential connections but also facilitates solutions that can be implemented in actual communities, towns, and cities.

Historically, investigators have assumed that "effectiveness research naturally and logically follows from successful efficacy research."[28] However, in practice, community health research is targeted

[22] P. A. Braveman, C. Cubbin, S. Egerter et al., "Socioeconomic Disparities in Health in the United States: What the Patterns Tell Us," *American Journal of Public Health* 100, suppl. 1 (2010): S186–S196.

[23] Institute of Medicine, *A Framework for Educating Health Professionals to Address the Social Determinants of Health* (Washington, DC: National Academies Press, 2016), 59, https://www.nap.edu/catalog/21923/a-framework-for-educating -health-professionals-to-address-the-social-determinants-of-health.

[24] World Health Organization Commission on the Social Determinants of Health, *Closing the Gap in a Generation. Health Equity through Action on the Social Determinants of Health* (Geneva: WHO, 2008, 9, http://apps.who.int/iris/ bitstream/10665/43943/1/9789241563703_eng.pdf.

[25] Koh et al., "Translating Research Evidence into Practice."

[26] Braveman et al., "Socioeconomic Disparities in Health," S193.

[27] Koh et al., "Translating Research Evidence into Practice," S73.

[28] R. E. Glasgow, E. Lichtenstein, and A. C. Marcus, "Why Don't We See More Translation of Health Promotion Research to Practice? Rethinking the Efficacy-to-Effectiveness Transition," *American Journal of Public Health* 93, no. 8 (2003): 1261–1267.

toward real-world outcomes. Efficacy studies involve standardized programs delivered uniformly to homogeneous, narrowly targeted research subjects. Efficacy trials assess whether a "program does more good than harm when delivered under optimum conditions."[29] In contrast, effectiveness studies test whether a "program does more good than harm when delivered under real-world conditions."[30] Thus, efficacy research and effectiveness research are disparate enterprises. The traditional model of translating research into practice, that is, "progressing from efficacy studies to effectiveness trials to dissemination projects,"[31] is flawed or incomplete when applied to public policy development.

One approach is the RE-AIM evaluation framework, which prioritizes public health issues.[32] The acronym RE-AIM stands for reach, efficacy or effectiveness, adoption, implementation, and maintenance:

- *Reach* refers to participation rate and the representativeness of study participants.
- *Adoption* refers to the representativeness of community settings or organizations that will conduct the program or intervention.
- *Maintenance* refers to the persistence of behavioral change at the individual level and "the extent to which a treatment or practice becomes institutionalized in an organization."[33]

The model balances emphasis on *internal validity* (efficacy studies) and *external validity* (effectiveness studies). The RE-AIM framework assists researchers in accounting for contextual factors or moderating factors, such as race/ethnicity, socioeconomic status, and type of setting, thus incorporating features of effectiveness studies into efficacy studies. By blending considerations of both internal validity and external validity, the RE-AIM model assists researchers and public policy planners to "select samples, interventions, settings, and agents" that will enhance the likelihood that findings of initial, more controlled studies will be reproduced in later, more widespread studies.[34]

Innovative research methods include *community-based participatory research* (CBPR),[35] which creates a partnership between university and institutional researchers and community members. CBPR is intended to foster development of interventions and protocols that will yield measurable benefit in terms of reducing health disparities and health inequities. Initial successes based on such strategic partnerships have been obtained in the United States and around the globe in countries such

---

[29] B. R. Flay, "Efficacy and Effectiveness Trials (and Other Phases of Research) in the Development of Health Promotion Programs," *Preventive Medicine* 15, no. 5 (1986): 451–474,

[30] Ibid.

[31] Glasgow, Lichtenstein, and Marcus, "Why Don't We See More Translation of Health Promotion Research to Practice?" 1262.

[32] R. E. Glasgow, T. M. Vogt, and S. M. Boles, "Evaluating the Public Health Impact of Health Promotion Interventions: The RE-AIM Framework," *American Journal of Public Health* 89, no. 9 (1999): 1322–1327.

[33] Glasgow, Lichtenstein, and Marcus, "Why Don't We See More Translation of Health Promotion Research to Practice?" 1263.

[34] Ibid., 1264.

[35] B. A. Israel, A. J. Schulz, E. A. Parker et al., "Review of Community-Based Research: Assessing Partnership Approaches to Improve Public Health," *Annual Review of Public Health* 19, no. 1 (1998): 173–202; L. Cacari-Stone, N. Wallerstein, A. P. Garcia et al., "The Promise of Community-Based Participatory Research for Health Equity: A Conceptual Model for Bridging Evidence with Policy," *American Journal of Public Health* 104, no. 9 (2014): 1615–1623.

as England,[36] Uganda,[37] and Ecuador.[38] In England, the Department of Health 2008 report indicated achievement of almost all policy commitments established in 2003. The 2008 report declared a new target of reducing inequalities in health outcomes by 10 percent by 2010 with respect to infant mortality and life expectancy. The 2016 estimated infant mortality rate in the United Kingdom was 4.3 per 1,000 live births,[39] reduced from 5.0 in 2005.[40] The 2016 estimated life expectancy in the United Kingdom was 80.7 years,[41] improved from 77.1 years in 2005.[42] In Uganda, in the remote and impoverished district of Kitgum, a multisectoral framework of national, district, and subcounty institutions acted to reduce cases of acute childhood malnutrition and stunting in the one-year period from 2005 to 2006. In Ecuador, in the municipality of Cotacachi, the activities of an intersector health council resulted in the elimination of maternal and child mortality in 2004, 2005, and 2006. In 2005 Cotacachi declared itself free from illiteracy, the multisectoral agencies having taught more than 6,000 illiterate people to read in approximately two years.

Overall, use of the social determinants approach to reducing and eliminating health disparities will require government leadership, innovative research protocols whose goal is to translate efficacy into effectiveness, and broad-based community participation. Ongoing ethical commitment to achieving health equity and continuing partnerships among communities, researchers, and governments will assist in establishing improved local, national, and global health and greater achievement of human flourishing.

Health Disparities/Health Inequities and LGBT Populations

Lesbian, gay, bisexual, and transgender (LBGT) persons experience unique health disparities and health inequities. In 2011, the IOM published *The Health of Lesbian, Gay, Bisexual, and Transgender People: Building a Foundation for Better Understanding*. The IOM report focused on the health of

---

[36] Department of Health, *Health Inequalities: Progress and Next Steps* (London: Department of Health, 2008), http://webarchive.nationalarchives.gov.uk/20130123194028/http://www.dh.gov.uk/en/Publicationsandstatistics/Publications/PublicationsPolicyAndGuidance/DH_085307.

[37] R. Mutambi, R. Hasunira, and V. Oringa, *Intersectoral Action on Health in a Conflict Situation. A Case Study of Kitgum District, Northern Uganda* (Geneva: WHO, 2007), http://www.who.int/social_determinants/resources/isa_conflict_uga.pdf.

[38] L. M. Vega, *Innovative Intersector Practices for Health and Equity. The Case of Cotacachi Ecuador* (Geneva: WHO, 2007), http://www.who.int/social_determinants/resources/isa_cotacachi_ecu.pdf.

[39] Central Intelligence Agency, *The World Factbook, 2017*, https://www.cia.gov/library/publications/the-world-factbook/rankorder/2091rank.html.

[40] Office for National Health Statistics, *Childhood, Infant and Perinatal Mortality in England and Wales: 2012*, https://www.ons.gov.uk/peoplepopulationandcommunity/birthsdeathsandmarriages/deaths/bulletins/childhoodinfantandperinatalmortalityinenglandandwales/2014-01-30.

[41] Central Intelligence Agency, *The World Factbook, 2017*, https://www.cia.gov/library/publications/the-world-factbook/rankorder/2102rank.html.

[42] Office for National Health Statistics, "National Life Tables, UK: 2013–2015," https://www.ons.gov.uk/peoplepopulationandcommunity/birthsdeathsandmarriages/lifeexpectancies/bulletins/nationallifetablesunitedkingdom/20132015.

sexual-minority populations and assessed current levels of scientific knowledge regarding the health status of LGBT populations.[43] The IOM report emphasized the need to collect more national data to "fully understand the health needs of U.S. LGBT populations."[44] The report noted that LGBT persons have been subject to discrimination within the healthcare system[45] As well, LGBT individuals are disproportionately affected by stigmatization and victimization.[46] In 2012, HHS published the HHS LGBT Issues Coordinating Committee 2012 Report.[47] The HHS report noted that research suggests that LGBT individuals and families may face significant disparities in access to healthcare and health coverage. HHS objectives in 2012 included informing the National Institutes of Health and the broader research community "about important areas in which to advance biomedical research on LGBT health."[48]

However, despite these initiatives, healthcare practitioners, healthcare service providers, and medical researchers report a lack of knowledge regarding health disparities and health inequities that impact LBGT populations.[49] Healthy People 2020 identified numerous health disparities affecting LBGT persons,[50] including the following:

- A higher prevalence of HIV infection, mental health issues, and suicide among transgender people
- LGBT populations have high rates of tobacco, alcohol, and other drug use
- Lesbians are less likely to obtain preventive services for cancer
- Lesbians and bisexual females are more likely to be overweight or obese
- LGBT youth are more likely to be homeless
- LGBT youth are two to three times more likely to attempt suicide
- Elderly LGBT individuals encounter additional barriers to health owing to isolation and a lack of social services and culturally competent providers

Health inequities impacting LGBT persons include lack of health insurance, fear of discrimination from providers, insufficient availability of healthcare providers with appropriate training in the health needs of LGBT individuals,[51] and decreased access to quality preventive care.[52]

---

[43] Institute of Medicine, *The Health of Lesbian, Gay, Bisexual, and Transgender People: Building a Foundation for Better Understanding* (Washington, DC: National Academies Press, 2011), http://www.nationalacademies.org/hmd/Reports/2011/The-Health-of-Lesbian-Gay-Bisexual-and-Transgender-People.aspx.

[44] Ibid., 132.

[45] Ibid., 75.

[46] J. W. Buckey and C. N. Browning, "Factors Affecting the LGBT Population When Choosing a Surrogate Decision Maker," *Journal of Social Services Research* 39, no. 2 (2013): 233–252.

[47] U.S. Department of Health and Human Services, *HHS LGBT Issues Coordinating Committee 2012 Report*, https://www.hhs.gov/programs/topic-sites/lgbt/enhanced-resources/reports/health-objectives-2012/index.html.

[48] Ibid.

[49] Buckey and Browning, "Factors Affecting the LGBT Population," 246.

[50] Healthy People 2020, *Lesbian, Gay, Bisexual, and Transgender Health*, https://www.healthypeople.gov/2020/topics-objectives/topic/lesbian-gay-bisexual-and-transgender-health.

[51] Institute of Medicine, *The Health of LGBT People*, 297.

[52] L. Mollon, "The Forgotten Minorities: Health Disparities of the Lesbian, Gay, Bisexual, and Transgendered Communities," *Journal of Health Care for the Poor and Underserved* 23, no. 1 (2012): 1–6.

To begin to redress health disparities and health inequities experienced by LGBT individuals, the IOM report recommended that the National Institutes of Health implement "a research agenda designed to advance knowledge and understanding of LGBT health."[53] Priority research areas included demographic research, health inequities, and transgender-specific health needs.[54] The IOM recommended that data on sexual orientation and gender identity be collected in federally funded surveys administered by HHS. As well, data on sexual orientation and gender identity should be collected in EHRs.[55] In terms of healthcare practice, providers are encouraged to use gender neutral language when discussing a patient's personal relationships. Further, healthcare practitioners should provide statements regarding equal treatment for all patients and include partners (per the patient's instructions) in treatment planning.[56] Standardized intake forms should include additional identifiers for sexual orientation, gender identity, and alternative family units.[57] Additionally, professional education of physicians, nurses, and allied healthcare providers should include specific training regarding how to better serve LGBT patients and how to redress health disparities and health inequities that affect LGBT persons.[58]

Bias in Healthcare Delivery

Bias (or prejudice) may be defined as an unjustified negative attitude toward another based on that person's group membership.[59] Health disparities/health inequities among members of racial/ethnic minorities, those in lower socioeconomic groups, and LGBT persons may often be perpetuated by bias in healthcare delivery.[60] As well, health disparities/health inequities exist in a "broader historical and contemporary context of social and economic inequality, prejudice, and systematic bias."[61]

Thus, healthcare providers, as all other persons, are likely influenced in their racial and ethnic attitudes by pervasive social trends.[62] Despite the explicit commitment to deliver care equally, some studies suggest that implicit stereotyping and bias on the part of healthcare providers can impact

[53] Institute of Medicine, *The Health of LGBT People*, 6.

[54] Ibid.

[55] Ibid., 9.

[56] K. A. Bonvicini and M. J. Perlin, "The Same but Different: Clinician-Patient Communication with Gay and Lesbian Patients," *Patient Education and Counseling* 51, no. 2 (2001): 115–22.

[57] Mollon, "The Forgotten Minorities," 4–5.

[58] Ibid., 5.

[59] B. D. Smedley, A. Y. Stith, and A. R. Nelson, eds., *Unequal Treatment: Confronting Racial and Ethnic Disparities in Health Care* (Washington, DC: National Academies Press, 2003), 10.

[60] E. N. Chapman, A. Kaatz, and M. Carnes, "Physicians and Implicit Bias: How Doctors May Unwittingly Perpetuate Health Care Disparities," *Journal of General Internal Medicine* 28, no. 11 (2013): 1504–1510.

[61] R. L. Johnson, S. Saha, J. J. Arbelaez et al., "Racial and Ethnic Differences in Patient Perceptions of Bias and Cultural Competence in Health Care," *Journal of General Internal Medicine* 19 (2004): 101–110.

[62] Smedley, Stith, and Nelson, *Unequal Treatment,* 490.

their judgment and behavior when they interact with stigmatized patients.[63] For example, evidence of implicit (unconscious) race bias among physicians was first formally documented in 2007.[64] Utilizing clinical vignettes of a "50-year-old male patient presenting to the emergency department with chest pain and an electrocardiogram suggestive of anterior myocardial infarction," physicians' implicit biases were strongly associated with treatment choices regarding thrombolysis (use of medication to dissolve clots formed in blood vessels). Specifically, as the degree of antiblack bias on a race preference *Implicit Association Test* (IAT)[65] increased, "recommendations for thrombolysis for black patients decreased."[66] As well, implicit bias against blacks (as measured by the race preference IAT) was "positively correlated with likelihood of recommending thrombolysis for white patients."[67] More recently, an assessment of the literature worldwide demonstrated that more than two-thirds of studies reviewed found evidence of racism among healthcare providers.[68] For example, eleven vignette-based studies found that "race influences the medical decision making of healthcare practitioners, whereas eight studies found no association."[69] Recommendations for redress included a "systematic approach to monitoring racism among healthcare providers" and concurrent implementation of evidence-based antiracism approaches that counter stereotypes, build empathy and perspective taking, develop personal responsibility, and "promote intergroup contact and intercultural understanding within healthcare settings."[70]

Importantly, members of racial/ethnic minorities report greater dissatisfaction with their healthcare providers, particularly when the providers are not of the same ethnicity/race, and perceive significantly more bias in healthcare delivery compared with whites.[71] Compared with whites, members of racial/ethnic minorities, including Hispanic Americans, African Americans, and Asian Americans, reported greater difficulty in communicating with their healthcare providers, were approximately fourteen times as likely to believe they would receive better healthcare if they were of a different race or ethnicity, and were more likely to feel treated with disrespect during a healthcare visit.[72]

---

[63] C. A. Zestcott, I. V. Blair, and J. Stone, "Examining the Presence, Consequences, and Reduction of Implicit Bias in Health Care: A Narrative Review," *Group Process and Intergroup Relations* 19, no. 4 (2016): 528–542, 529.

[64] A. R. Green, D. R. Carney, D. J. Pallin et al., "Implicit Bias among Physicians and Its Prediction of Thrombolysis Decisions for Black and White Patients," *Journal of General Internal Medicine* 22, no. 9 (2007): 1231–1238.

[65] A. G. Greenwald, D. E. McGhee, and J. L. K. Schwartz, "Measuring Individual Differences in Implicit Social Cognition: The Implicit Association Test," *Journal of Personality and Social Psychology* 74, no. 6 (1998): 1464–1480.

[66] Green et al., "Implicit Bias among Physicians," 1235.

[67] Ibid., 1237.

[68] Y. Paradies, M. Truong, and N. Priest, "A Systematic Review of the Extent and Measurement of healthcare provider racism," *Journal of General Internal Medicine* 29, no. 2 (2014): 364–387.

[69] Ibid., 383.

[70] Ibid.

[71] Zestcott, Blair, and Stone, "Examining the Presence, Consequences, and Reduction of Implicit Bias in Health Care," 529.

[72] K. S. Collins, D. L. Hughes, M. M. Doty et al., *Diverse Communities, Common Concerns: Assessing Health Care Quality for Minority Americans. Findings from the Commonwealth Fund 2001 Health Care Quality Survey* (Washington, DC: Commonwealth Fund, 2002), http://www.commonwealthfund.org/publications/fund-reports/2002/mar/diverse-communities —common-concerns—assessing-health-care-quality-for-minorityamericans.

As well, regarding LGBT persons, sexual minority status is "a marker of elevated risk for mental, physical, and sexual health problems."[73] The health of LGBT individuals may be compromised by chronic stress associated with minority status, legal barriers to health insurance, providers who receive minimal training in culturally competent care of LGBT persons, and experiences and expectations of discrimination within the healthcare system.[74] As an example of healthcare provider bias, research has demonstrated that "implicit preferences for heterosexual over lesbian and gay people are pervasive among a majority of health care providers."[75] Further, implicit stereotyping of LGBT older adults persists in the healthcare delivery system, and "these biases contribute to health disparities."[76] Such nonconscious stereotyping may manifest in acts of victimization and discrimination, as when "a transgender patient is denied care or when a hospital fails to allow a same-sex life partner to be at the patient's bedside in the intensive care unit."[77] Overall, for all individuals, such experiences of bias encountered in the delivery of healthcare services are likely to influence subsequent interactions with the healthcare community and may lead even to the avoidance of needed care.[78]

Recommendations for remedying bias include increasing the proportion of underrepresented U.S. racial and ethnic minorities among healthcare professionals and promoting consistency and equity of care through use of evidence-based guidelines.[79] Most professional educational interventions utilize a two-step approach that includes (1) making students aware of their implicit biases and (2) providing instruction in strategies "to either reduce the activation of implicit associations, or control how those associations influence judgment and behavior."[80] Strategies employed include bias awareness strategies, control strategies, and perspective-taking strategies. For example, control strategies are directed toward controlling automatic responses to members of minority groups and utilizing affirming egalitarian goals, seeking common-group identities, and relating to the patient as an individual via counterstereotyping.[81] As well, bias reduction should be promoted at the institutional level by utilizing positive intergroup contact across group boundaries, that is, across provider–patient and student-faculty boundaries.[82] The ultimate goal of training students and healthcare professionals to reduce implicit bias "is to reverse the disparities in care that many stigmatized patient groups receive."[83] [...]

---

[73] J. A. Sabin, R. G. Riskind, and B. A. Nosek, "Health Care Providers' Implicit and Explicit Attitudes Toward Lesbian Women and Gay Men," *American Journal of Public Health* 105, no. 9 (2015): 1831–1841.

[74] Ibid., 1831.

[75] Ibid., 1840.

[76] M. B. Foglia and K. I. Fredriksen-Goldsen, "Health Disparities among LGBT Older Adults and the Role of Nonconscious Bias," *Hastings Center Report* 44, no. 5 (2014): S40–S44.

[77] Ibid., S42.

[78] Ibid., S43.

[79] Smedley, Stith, and Nelson, *Unequal Treatment,* 20.

[80] Zestcott, Blair, and Stone, "Examining the Presence, Consequences, and Reduction of Implicit Bias in Health Care," 535.

[81] Ibid.

[82] Ibid., 536.

[83] Ibid., 537.

Summary

This unit emphasizes how healthcare workers need a broad appreciation of justice. Implementing justice requires apprehending its many layers and its effects. An understanding of justice as fairness informs social structures and directs policy formation and individual action.

Recall Vern's situation. As Vern ponders how to manage his patients' needs, he evaluates the benefits and burdens that confront the clinic. He has both limited resources and obligations to his patients. Vern's goals are to provide quality care and to attend to the needs of his patients. Justice as fairness requires an equal distribution, yet he realizes that some patients' disabilities require more attention than others. The stakes are high; the integrity of the clinic and Vern's fiduciary obligations to the patients are on the line.

Vern's situation exposes how justice as fairness goes beyond procedures that promote the equal distribution of goods. In Vern's case, justice is much more than the equal distribution of resources. When resources are limited, individual differences must be taken into account. Equality, giving people the same share, is important. However, justice must also be matched to individuals' health needs and account for a constellation of factors, including need, capabilities, contribution, merit, socioeconomic factors, and what we deserve.

The fulfillment of justice requires acknowledging and addressing disparities in health outcomes, health policies, individual attitudes, and the social determinants of health. The healthcare system can promote justice by articulating clear standards of fairness and nondiscrimination. These standards apply to employees as well as patients and consumers. Prejudice and unfairness are built into the fabric of society and must be removed.

Justice involves more than nondiscrimination and a standard for the allocation of resources and nondiscrimination. Justice must also account for hidden bias and the disadvantages we experience. We must build a strong foundation, one that avoids false beliefs, antiquated attitudes, and a lack of knowledge. Think about how you will provide care in light of this critical evaluation of justice. Keep in mind the presence of health disparities within the healthcare system. Justice as fairness moves beyond procedural norms and must acknowledge our differences. Justice calls us to action.

Comprehension Questions

Buechler, *The Social Construction of Race*

1. What are four reasons that challenge assumptions about the biological basis of race?

2. How does discrimination sustain the social construction of race?

3. Describe the traditional and institutional models of discrimination.

4. What is color-blind racism?

Lemberg, *Health Disparities/Health Inequities*

1. Distinguish between the terms "disparity," "inequality," and "inequity."

2. What are the major differences between a health disparity and a health inequity?

3. What are some proposed strategies for addressing implicit bias in healthcare?

4. How does bias perpetuate unequal treatment in healthcare?

Vern's Story

Developing Your Moral Imagination: Critical Thinking Questions

1. If you were in a similar situation to Vern, how would you help your patients? On what basis would you make your decision?

2. In the context of justice, what should you think about when you have to make decisions that affect the care of patients?

3. Does justice as fairness mean treating people equally all the time? How might equality all at times be unfair?

4. How should we interpret a call to justice in healthcare?

5. What obligations do providers have to respond to injustice?

Reflections on Crisis: The Lived Experience of Illness

Otto's Story

Otto, a physical therapist, treats patients recovering from injuries that cause permanent damage, disability, and lack of functionality. He enjoys helping patients return to everyday activities and is accustomed to the challenges of working with individuals whose impairments have upended their daily lives. Otto is currently working with Greta, a patient with a severely torn ACL that surgery could not completely repair. Greta remains a healthy middle-aged woman, but due to the injury, her days of competitive running have ended. Greta is an extremely difficult patient. She is not responding to treatment, she is frustrated by Otto's attempts to help manage her disability, and she is unwilling to communicate with him. Otto struggles to relate to Greta; he does not understand why she is so discouraged and angry. Otto tries to be optimistic. He tells her that the postsurgical pain will eventually cease, and she will regain her strength. In time, she will walk and not need an assistive device. Otto is repeatedly taxed by Greta's miserable attitude, and he does not know how to help her.

Schema Activation/Response Question

What values should guide Otto as he works with Greta?

Cultivating Professional Values

The APTA core values aim to promote good reasoning. The key values at stake in Otto's story include:

- **Accountability:** taking responsibility for one's actions and choices
- **Altruism:** sacrificing for others and putting others' needs before your own
- **Collaboration:** working together in pursuit of a shared goal
- **Duty:** fulfilling one's commitment to the profession and meeting the public's trust
- **Excellence:** possessing knowledge and skill and acquiring habits of lifelong learning
- **Integrity:** acting in accord with one's personal and professional moral identity
- **Social Responsibility:** doing good for others and helping the larger community

Introduction to the Topic

This unit explores the principal experience of patients: illness. We analyze the nature of illness and explore how maladies affect more than the physiological and psychological functions of the human body. Indeed, the crisis of illness affects one's very sense of self. Any crisis forces us to make important decisions. When we are ill-prepared, what kind of response is reasonable?

A crisis can assume many forms, but all crises threaten to destabilize us. The crisis of illness, in particular, can jeopardize our personal identities, values, and life goals. For patients, the process of restarting one's life after a crisis can be overwhelming and unnerving.

Introduction to the Reading

The reading by contemporary philosopher Fredrik Svenaeus, "What is Phenomenology of Medicine?: Embodiment, Illness, and Being-in-the-World," considers the lived experience of illness and disability. Svenaeus shows these maladies are more than abnormal physiology, more than biological facts and features. He employs a phenomenological methodology to examine illness and disability. To understand their meaning, Svenaeus claims that we must look at the lived reality of these experiences.

Svenaeus discusses how our bodily experiences extend beyond scientific explanation. To understand the human body simply as a constellation of biological processes is to overlook the "first-person-perspective" of illness. Svenaeus claims that "the body is my point of view, and my way of experiencing and understanding the world." When people are ill, they feel the world differently. Physiological abnormalities affect our bodies, but as we are "embodied creatures," these abnormalities also affect our selves. We must recognize that the person in the sick body must change how they inhabit the world.

Svenaeus distinguishes between "homelike" and "unhomelike" being-in-the-world. The former refers to a state of health, or well-being, even if one suffers from disease or disability. In a "homelike" state, a person feels comfortable in their body and in the world. "Unhomelike" refers to a feeling of alienation; a person suffers from a disruption of the unity between their embodied self and the physical world. In this state, their impairment restricts them from fulfilling their values and goals.

Svenaeus illuminates how illness and disability create a personal struggle within the self. In light of his phenomenological study, an alternative perspective on illness and disability arises; they are seen as an impairment of one's sense of personal identity. While the concepts of illness and disability include biological aspects, Svenaeus urges the reader to acknowledge the experiential nature of such maladies. The experience of illness and disability are not purely physical struggles.

What is Phenomenology of Medicine?

Embodiment, Illness and Being-in-the-World

By Fredrik Svenaeus

T he question of my [reading]'s title involves two issues that have to be settled before moving on to the main topic, the phenomenology of medicine: the issue of what phenomenology itself might be, certainly, and I will return to that shortly; but no less important, the issue of what medicine is.

Medicine

So, what is medicine? What is its essence and how are its borders with other human activities to be delineated? As everyone who has pursued the field of philosophy of medicine knows, the exact nature and border of medicine is itself a constant topic of debate. I myself would defend a concept of medicine that stresses the *meeting* of health care professional and patient in an interpretative attempt to help and treat the ill and suffering one, whereas others would look rather for the essence of medicine in the *application* of medical knowledge in attempts to understand and alter the biological organism (Svenaeus 2000b). These two answers to the question of what medicine is do not necessarily exclude each other; they could be brought into dialogue, and the first answer could be made to include the second, just as the second answer could be complemented by the first. The interpretative practice of understanding and helping the patient could, and, indeed, should, include biological knowledge, while the applied biology paradigm would need to address, in some way, that the doctor sees a person and not only the person's body.

Despite the possibility of combining the two alternatives, where one puts the major stress will be important, not only in answering the question of whether or not a particular activity is to be counted as a medical activity, but also in addressing ethical and political questions concerning the mission of medicine today and in the future. If medicine is an interpretative, helping meeting between persons aiming to restore or protect health and alleviate the suffering of illness, the practice *itself* will have ethical roots, whereas if medicine is the application of medical knowledge in a clinical context, medicine will have to be encouraged to grow ethical branches on its morally neutral tree, so to speak. Towards the end of this [reading], I will return briefly to the issue of what medicine is in itself, but first I will focus on the second issue mentioned above, that of phenomenology. What is phenomenology?

Phenomenology

A preliminary answer to this question can be provided by stating that phenomenology can be considered a kind of *first philosophy* seeking the *foundations* of ontological and epistemological questions by returning to *lived experience* (Spiegelberg 1982). Phenomenology has branched out into many additional disciplines from its inception about 100 years ago with Edmund Husserl, and continued through the work of philosophers like Martin Heidegger, Maurice Merleau-Ponty and Jean-Paul Sartre. Scholars and researchers of art, literature, psychology, sociology, anthropology and history, and recently also nursing and medicine, have tried to make use of the methodology of "going back to the phenomena themselves and abstaining from any taken for granted views in studying them", as it was put by Husserl (Toombs 2001a).

The expression "the phenomena themselves" is understood by Husserl and his followers as that which shows itself in the experiences we are all having all the time. The starting point is not the world of science but the meaning structures of the everyday world, what the phenomenologist calls the "life world". The phenomenologist shows experience itself to be meaningful in the sense that experience is always had by someone, a subject, and that it displays a content for the one who is having the experience (that which I am conscious of: the object). The apple tree in Husserl's back garden has a shape and a colour, a "treeness", or even an "appletreeness", that stands out and shows itself against the horizon of the whole garden: on the lawn, beside the bushes, under the sky. The things that show up to us are thus embedded in horizons of meaning that allow them to show themselves as such-and-such things (Zahavi 2003).

Husserl was not particularly interested in botany but used the tree found in his garden to describe how all things in the life world show up in a spatially organized manner, having front and back sides, having colours, and so on. Phenomena show up to us as meaningful for us; they show up as things with different meaning contents. Surely there was a time for the newborn baby when everything was chaos, but experience soon takes on shape in being had by someone (the baby) and being about something (the breast). The baby is then, step-by-step, invited to the life world we all live in together with its rich meaning structures (for a good introduction to contemporary phenomenology acknowledging the developmental perspective, see Gallagher 2005).

This does not mean that experience does not sometimes have to be interpreted (what do I really see here?) or even re-evaluated (we make mistakes), or that the life world contours of some people are not richer than those of others (I can identify perhaps thirty birds, a skilled ornithologist can identify three hundred), but these nuances of the finely woven web of life world meanings should not fool us into assuming that the world is basically some kind of senseless raw matter out of which humans can construct any contents they want. Nor should it fool us into assuming that the only real structure of the world that there is, is the one we find (or construct) when we dive into the world of science. The life world comes first, the phenomenologist will claim, and this insight protects us from the exaggerations and mistakes of idealism and dualism as well as materialism and naturalism.

Phenomenology of Medicine

A phenomenologist can direct her attention to any phenomenon found worthy of study, and this is also the way phenomenology branches out into different disciplines beyond the very basic philosophical themes of being and knowledge *per se*. What experiences, then, are particularly relevant for the phenomenologist of medicine to explore? I will offer some examples of phenomena that I think are central to a phenomenology of medicine, and, indeed, to medicine itself, and although I do not intend my list to be exhaustive, I hope it is relevant to the way the phenomenology of medicine has developed so far. The most important contemporary studies to be mentioned in this relatively young field of study are, I think, the ones by Richard Zaner (1981), Drew Leder (1990), Kay Toombs (1992), Hans-Georg Gadamer ([1993] 1996), Fredrik Svenaeus (2000b) and Havi Carel (2008).

In the strict sense, the phenomenology of medicine is certainly a young field of study, but the issue of how old the field is depends on what topics you take to be medical topics. We find this [reading]'s first example of a topic central to the phenomenology of medicine, namely the ways of the body, dating back to the middle period of Husserl's phenomenology, the 1910s. The phenomenology of the body is analysed in more detail by Maurice Merleau-Ponty in the 1930s and 1940s ([1945] 1962), and it is brought up in connection with medical matters by phenomenologists such as F. J. J. Buytendijk, Hans Jonas, Herbert Plügge and Erwin Straus in the 1950s and 1960s (Spiegelberg 1972).

Embodiment

It is very important to medicine that we are *embodied* creatures—medicine explores the body and tries to understand how it functions in order to be able to fix it when it breaks, to put it very crudely. This is not all there is to medicine, but the knowledge of bodily processes is surely central to the medical project. Everybody has a body—a body that can be of great joy, but also of great suffering and pain to its bearer. The fundamental point that the phenomenologist would emphasize here is that not only does everybody *have* a body, everybody *is* a body. What is the difference?

When we say that every experience is embodied, this means that the body is my point of view, and my way of experiencing and understanding the world. Not only can I experience my own body as an *object* of my experience—when I feel it or touch it or look at it in the mirror—but the body also harbours, on the subjective side of experience, the proprioceptive and kinaesthetic schemas that make a person's experiences possible in the first place. The body is my place in the world—the place where I am which moves with me—which is also the zero-point that makes space and the place of things that I encounter possible at all. The body, as a rule, does not show itself to us in our experiences; it *withdraws* and so opens up a focus in which it is possible for things in the world to show up to us in different meaningful ways. When I speak to another person I am not attending to the way my body feels and moves, I am focused upon *her* and the things I am trying to communicate to her; this is made possible, however, by the way my body silently performs in the background. The body already organizes my experiences on a subconscious level. Proprioceptively it makes me present in the world, and kinaesthetically it allows me to experience the things that are not me—the things of the world that show up to my moving, sensing body in different activities through which they attain their place and significance.

Thus phenomenology can be understood as transgressing any dualistic picture of a soul living in and directing the ways of the body like some ghost in a machine. The body is me. But phenomenology is also—and this is even more important—fundamentally and from its beginning an anti-naturalistic project; that is, the phenomenologist would also contest any attempt to reduce experience to material processes only. Experience, to the phenomenologist, must be studied by acknowledging its meaning and content for the one who is *having* the experience. It is certainly possible to study experience from the third-person perspective of science also—we could study the ways light rays trigger nerve firings in my brain by way of the retina when I look at a person right now (if we hook me up to a technological device), but this picture of my brain in action would not be the experience of "me looking at her right now". The picture could catch neither the "me-ness" nor the content of the experience that I am having—this is the first-person perspective, which the phenomenologist takes as the starting point of the analysis. The phenomenologist would not contest that the scientific explanations of experiences made by way of scientific third-person-perspective investigations could be important in informing us about the workings of the world and ourselves, but she would deny that such scientific explanations could compensate for, or replace, first-person-perspective explorations of the experiences in question. In order to see this more clearly, let us now move on to my next example of a topic central to the phenomenology of medicine: illness.

Illness

As mentioned above, normally, when we move around in the world, acting, speaking, thinking and feeling, we do not pay any attention to our bodies. They perform their duties silently in the background, not only proprioceptively and kinaesthetically, but also as regards all the autonomic functions of our visceral life—breathing, our hearts beating, stomachs and bowels working, and so on. Sometimes, however, the body *shows up* in resisting and disturbing our efforts. It plagues us and demands our attention. A paradigm example is pain. If I have a headache it becomes hard to concentrate and think. Even before my attention is directed towards the headache itself, the whole world and all my projects become tinted by pain. When I read, the letters become fuzzy, the text itself hurts in me trying to understand it. This is Jean-Paul Sartre's example from *Being and Nothingness* (1956), published originally in 1943—so the phenomenology of illness, like the phenomenology of embodiment, actually goes back further than the contemporary studies mentioned above. Illness is never Sartre's main object of study, however; it is used mainly as an example to address questions of being and human nature in general (Svenaeus 2009).

Illness, as the headache example of Sartre already shows, displays a "mooded" aspect tied to activities one is performing. Other examples of illness moods are nausea, unmotivated tiredness or the way the body resists my attempts to do different things—like when I try to climb the stairs and my chest hurts. Of course, there are distinctions to be made here. For most people, the chest starts to hurt after five flights of fast climbing, but when it does so more or less immediately or unexpectedly, it is a paradigm example of illness. According to another very influential phenomenologist, Martin Heidegger, every experience we have is, as a matter of fact, attuned—"mooded"—but this attunement of our being-in-the-world normally, just like the embodied character of experience, stays in the subconscious background, not making itself known to us. In illness, however, the mood we are in makes itself known in penetrating our entire experience, finally, when it becomes unbearable, bringing us back to our plagued embodiment, which now resists our attempts to act and carry out things, instead of supporting them in the silent, enigmatic manner of healthy being-in-the-world (Gadamer 1996).

I have tried in earlier works to characterize and to a certain extent delineate the borders of such illness experiences by way of the concept of "unhomelike being-in-the-world" (Svenaeus 2000b). The life world is usually my home territory, but in illness this homelikeness gives in and takes on a rather *unhomelike* character, rooted in thwarted ways of being embodied. It is the mission of health care professionals to try to understand such unhomelike being-in-the-world and bring it back to homelikeness again, or at least closer to a home-being. This involves, but cannot be reduced to, ways of understanding and altering the physiological organism of the person who is ill. Health care professionals must also address everyday life matters of patients with a phenomenological eye, addressing and trying to understand the being-in-the-world of the person's life, which has turned unhomelike in illness. [...].

Illness, Disease and Disability

It is important to understand the fundamental difference between a phenomenological illness concept and the concept of disease as it is usually understood. A disease is a disturbance of the biological functions of the body (or something that causes such a disturbance), which can only be detected and understood from the third-person perspective of the doctor investigating the body with the aid of her hands or medical technologies. The patient can also, by way of the doctor, or by way of medical theory, or, as often happens nowadays, by way of a webpage on the internet, adopt such a third-person perspective towards her own body and speculate about diseases responsible for her suffering. But the suffering itself is an illness experience of the person who is in a world, embodied and connected to other people around her. Illness has meaning, or, perhaps we should say instead, *disturbs* the meaning processes of being-in-the-world in which one is leading one's life on an everyday level.

Typically, when I experience illness, my biological organism will be diseased, but there are possibilities of being ill without any detectable diseases, or of leading a homelike life, when suddenly the doctor finds a disease (e.g., by way of a cancer screening). The phenomenologist would stress that the full importance and content of illness can be attained only if the doctor, in addition to being skilled in diagnosing diseases, also affords attention to the experience, the being-in-the-world, of the patient. The life of the person (and not only the life of her biological organism) is, as a matter of fact, the reason why diseases *matter* to us as human beings—because they can make our lives miserable and even make us perish. If this were not the case, we would not *care* so much about them. It is because we want to be at home in the world that we study disease agents and try to find remedies for them, even though I suspect we will never succeed completely in this project, since unhomelikeness in its different forms seems to be a necessary part of human life. In a sense our vulnerability and finitude is exactly what makes us human (Heidegger talks about "being-towards-death" as constitutive for our being-in-the-world) so if medical science succeeds in making us invulnerable the creatures in question would not be human, but rather post-human beings.

The distinction between the embodied self and the world it is living in can also help us to understand the possibility of chronic maladies (not only diseases, but also injuries or congenital defects) without illness—that is, the cases of chronically afflicted persons who nevertheless enjoy a homelike being-in-the-world. In the phenomenological sense, these persons, most often referred to as chronically ill or disabled, would not, indeed, be unhealthy. These persons have managed to make adjustments in the meaning patterns of their selves and environments, sometimes assisted by medical professionals and medical therapies, or by other helpers, in ways that compensate for the maladies that they are suffering from. In other words, they have managed to make their being-in-the-world homelike again by way of changing not only the outer circumstances, but also their understanding of themselves in this altered situation. In the case of congenital defect, this possible adjustment to homelike being-in-the-world would take place through a process similar to how every normal child makes itself at home in the world, but needing more help and sometimes medical assistance (Svenaeus 2003).

The prospects of adjusting to a homelike being-in-the-world through a reinterpretation of the self and its situation in life depend partly on the person afflicted by the malady and partly on how severe the malady in question is. Some congenital defects, injuries or diseases might be so severe that a homelike being-in-the-world is not possible, while some maladies might be mild enough to allow for a homelike existence. The point of the phenomenological theory is, indeed, to find the starting point in the person and her life world circumstances, not in her biology, when it comes to questions of health and illness. This approach is not meant to exclude biology, however. The physiology of the body certainly afflicts and sets limits to the different ways we are able to experience and interpret our being-in-the-world. To develop a phenomenological theory of illness and health is therefore not meant as an attempt to replace biomedical research. In light of the successful history of modern medicine, this would certainly be an absurd project. Phenomenology is meant to enrich our understanding of health and illness in adding a level that addresses the questions of how the physiological processes and states are lived as meaningful in a culture.

That homelike being-in-the-world—and this, in the phenomenological theory, means health—is a possibility for some chronically diseased and disabled persons, helps us to discern different ways of promoting homelikeness for the ill. Biological therapy forms one very important way, since the curing of diseases tends to eradicate the unhomelikeness of illness more or less directly in many cases—think of an appendectomy, for instance. Medical rehabilitation—focusing on changing the self-understanding of patients, improving their mental and physical abilities and making adjustments in their life environments—forms the next step in the treatment of, for instance, a stroke. But the possibility of homelikeness for the disabled also has a social and political dimension. This is indeed why we have officially chosen the term *disabled* instead of *handicapped* when it comes to maladies other than diseases, such as congenital defects and injuries. To establish homelikeness requires resources for building environments in which the disabled can make adjustments for their functional disabilities. But it also takes *respect* for forms of life that differ from the normal one, which can be just as homelike but nevertheless very different from ours—think of Deaf culture, for instance. The being at home or not being at home with one's own body depends not only on life world patterns that make it easier or harder to move and perceive (e.g., using a wheelchair, being deaf or blind), but also on attitudes: that is, how the disabled are met, looked upon and assigned a worth or non-worth by others.

Does it make sense to say that every form of obtrusive embodiment could be compensated for, in terms of homelikeness or unhomelikeness, by changing the meaning patterns of the world that the disabled (like all other persons) rely on in their being-in? Can we always compensate for a non-standard embodiment by creating a non-standard world to be in? This seems to be an empirical question, but allow me to say that I think the words "normal" and "standard" make sense not only in discussing embodiment but also in discussing the meaning patterns of the world from a phenomenological point of view. There are overlapping patterns of cultural consistency in life world patterns, and these seem to be tied, among other things, to our shared ways of embodiment. But there are also great variances in cultural patterns that make different forms of diseases and disabilities easier or harder to live with. Studies by social anthropologists such as Arthur Kleinman bear clear evidence of this (e.g., Kleinman 1995).

To sum up: health consists of a homelike being-in-the-world. Home-likeness is supposed to capture the character of the normal, unapparent, transparency of everyday activities, *not* of feeling happy. Health in phenomenology is meant as a first-person concept, in contrast to a third-person concept of health, which would offer the definition of health rather as simply the absence of all diseases and other maladies. It is possible to be healthy—to enjoy a homelike being-in-the-world—even if the person in question suffers from some kind of malady. This means that being phenomenologically healthy might include being abnormal, either in the physiological sense or in the sense of demanding a non-standard world to be in.

That a diseased or disabled person can, in some cases, with the help of medical assistance, political efforts or hard work on her part enjoy a homelike being-in-the-world, points towards the importance of including a consideration of the ill person's life world in the activities and abilities of health care professionals. But it also illustrates that homelike and unhomelike being-in-the-world are not mutually exclusive phenomena, but rather dimensionally opposed tendencies that characterize our entire being-in. Even healthy life is unhomelike to some extent, though not in ways that are tied to plagued embodiment. Ill life is unhomelike to different *extents* and in different *ways*, depending on diagnosis, person and opportunities to make adaptations in being-in, but in all these embodied forms of not being at home, the ill life always retains some elements of homelikeness if it did not, it is doubtful it could be considered a being-in-the-world at all.

What has struck me as more and more important in my attempts to understand illness from the phenomenological point of view is the importance to health of being able to *adapt* to an altered embodiment and environment in order to stay healthy or become healthy again, when life is obstructed by diseases or other threatening events. This might be the true health, the great health that Nietzsche was talking about and claimed to be enjoying despite his dreadful physiology (Krell 1996). To become homelike in the face of unhomelikeness: this would be the health in illness. The illness in health would be the tendency to fall into unhomelikeness very easily, and to have great difficulties in regaining the homelike state again.

Medical Technologies

The development of modern medical science in the last two hundred years or so has made it possible for us to intervene in our own biology in new and stunning ways. Not only is it now possible for us to cure and prevent many diseases from which people previously died *en masse* or were crippled for life, it is also increasingly possible to enhance our biology beyond the boundaries of restoring normality. Medical technology (gene technology and psychopharmacology, for instance) is now stepping onto the stage of self-transformation, making us become "better than well", to quote the title of a book by Carl Elliott (2003). This process is problematic and has given rise to high expectations as well as worries about the future of humankind. What contributions could phenomenology offer to this bioethical debate?

In its stress on encouraging doctors to focus on the ill person—the being-in-the-world of the patient—and not only on diseases, one can already sense a certain critique from the perspective of the phenomenologist towards a medicine in the hands of techno-science. The patient is, indeed, a subject, not only an object, and health care professionals must never forget this if they are to be successful in doing their job: helping ill people. This does not mean that a phenomenologist would recommend that doctors be less scientific in the sense of less knowledgeable in the field of diseases, only that the doctor must be able to establish contact between this medical, scientific gaze and the meeting with the patient as an ill person. This goes for nearly all kinds of health professionals: even surgeons need an eye for the life world dimension of the patient, as Oliver Sacks shows in his autobiographical story *A Leg to Stand On* (1984).

Technology development and application has a tendency to live a life of its own: it takes over the scene, sets its own goals, and by these means alters the scope of normality. It is very hard to resist new technology, since as soon as a technology has been introduced, the situation of choice has already been altered. If we say no to a technology—for example, an early ultrasound test to detect the risk that a foetus might suffer from Down's syndrome—we must do so from an analysis of what the technology in question *could* lead to. It could lead to a world with less tolerance for abnormalities and weaknesses and a more hostile attitude towards people who choose to have babies who will be a burden to society. But, as the proponents of the technology will say, the technology does not *have to* have these feared consequences, maybe many parents will choose not to have an abortion and will welcome the child—suffering from Down's syndrome or not. Let the individuals make their own informed choices, the technology proponent will say. The answer to this from the technology sceptic will be that the individuals are not really able to make any informed choice, lacking relevant experience in the issue, and also that in reality, the risk assessment will lead to a lot of foetuses being aborted without actually having Down's syndrome. Yes, the technology proponent will admit, the test *could* have these consequences, but in order to avoid them let us work to improve the technology and the information for patients about the risk assessment. This is the only thing we can do, since who are *you* to refuse to let other people make their own choices? We live in a liberal, democratic society, don't we?

At this point, I think the phenomenologist could enter the scene with some valuable contributions to make to the rather polarized and unfruitful debate. The evaluation of medical technologies must be supplemented by a different type of analysis than the consequentialist–libertarian one I have just mapped out, if we are to be able to understand what technological development does to us. This analysis must focus on technologies as a part of our *mindset*; it must explore how the life world of people is altered by the technologies and the driving forces putting them to work. One such force is the market economy, but this is not all there is to the impact of new medical technologies in transforming our understanding of the world and ourselves. We are increasingly becoming objects of a technological gaze that we are making our own. Heidegger in the 1950s called this "*Gestell*"—a framing of our world by science through which everything consequently shows up as calculable and usable (Heidegger [1954] 1977). Heidegger, in his essays on technology, talked about forests, rivers and nuclear technology subjecting us to the *Gestell*, but the true extension of his analysis is the recent developments of gene technology, in which humankind itself is becoming the manipulated, not only the manipulator (Svenaeus 2007).

In my view, the most important thing in a contemporary phenomenological analysis of medical technology is to not fall into the trap of fear and hostility towards technology, something that is very visible, if not in Heidegger himself, then in many of his followers. It is obvious that many medical technologies, if kept within the bounds of sound judgement and application, are too valuable to our lives to be abstained from, although they do force people to take a stand on and possibly change their attitudes towards themselves and their own bodies. Organ transplantation is a good example. It harbours a tendency to resourcify and maybe even commodify our bodies—or at least parts of them, the organs—but the possibilities it offers in saving and healing lives are too valuable to say no to (Svenaeus 2010). The important thing in every case must be to make visible the mindset-transforming aspect of the technologies in question and relate this to the ethics and politics of technology use. "Control" appears to be a central concept in this phenomenological analysis. Who is in control of the technology? And how does the technology change our need to increasingly *be in control* of everything in our life? Can this urge for control also make our lives less worth living in the sense that we no longer have a place for the unexpected and unplanned? Or is it merely like making our roads safer by means of wider lanes, better fences and speed limits, protecting ourselves from unwanted dangers, making our lives longer? [...].

Summary

Clinicians possess the knowledge and skills to treat injury, illness, disease, and disability. However, are providers prepared to heal the harm caused by the lived experiences of illness?

Acknowledging the embodied nature of illness can be the first step in the rehabilitation process. Indeed, healers and caregivers have a duty to acknowledge the nonmedical and nonphysiological dimensions of illness and disability.

Recall Otto's dilemma. How can he help Greta? He must understand the nature of Greta's experience of disability. She is not only physically impaired, but her values and her identity are also in a state of emergency. Greta's injury has forced a dramatic and permanent change upon her. She feels alienated by her impairment, and she must redefine herself. Greta is challenged by the crisis and must find new ways to fulfill her values and pursue her goals.

Otto realizes that he must treat more than Greta's physiological injuries and impairments. He must also attend to her humanity. He realizes Greta's struggle lies deeper than the physical; she is estranged from her body. His relationship with Greta cannot be merely transactional, and he cannot define her based on her physiological condition.

During his next session with Greta, Otto skips the usual therapeutic plan of care. He decides to interview her for another patient history, but instead of inquiring about her physical condition, Otto asks about her history of running and lifestyle prior to her injury. In order to better treat her, Otto steps back from his plan of care to learn more about Greta's life.

Providers need to cultivate skills that treat the whole person. Patients are individuals with different life histories, goals, and values. While objectivity is important, clinicians must see their patients as people and not simply as bodies that need to be fixed. When healthcare workers have not experienced illness or disability themselves, they are often unable to understand the perspective of their patients. By recognizing the nonphysiological experience of illness, providers can communicate better and identify treatment plans that meet patient needs.

Ethical guidance is essential when responding to crises. Professional ethical standards help providers fulfill their moral and fiduciary obligations. Although understanding your values is a good place to start, it is not enough. Clinicians need a clear blueprint for action. In order to be effective, caregivers also need to understand their patient's values and nonclinical needs. Providers must listen to the testimony of their patients and attune themselves to the entirety of their humanity, and not just medically relevant information.

Comprehension Questions

Svenaeus, *What is Phenomenology of Medicine?*: *Embodiment, Illness, and Being-in-the-World*

1. What is phenomenology of medicine?
2. What is embodiment?
3. How does the author describe the experience of illness?
4. What is the difference between the embodied self and the world?

Otto's Story

Developing Your Moral Imagination: Critical Thinking Questions

1. What values should guide Otto's actions?
2. Have you experienced severe illness or disability that impaired your ability to carry out your life goals? How did you handle it?
3. As a clinician, how can you help patients recover their sense of self when confronted by long-term illness or disability?
4. What are the goals of healthcare?
5. What values should form the foundation of healthcare practice?

ADDITIONAL READINGS

Additional Readings for Unit I

Beauchamp, Tom L., and James F. Childress. *Principles of Biomedical Ethics*. 6th ed. Oxford University Press, 2009.

Kittay, Eva Feder. *Love's Labor: Essays on Women, Equality, and Dependency*, 2nd ed. Routledge, 2020.

Rachels, James. *The Elements of Moral Philosophy*, 8th ed. McGraw-Hill, 2014.

Additional Readings for Unit II

Blanton, Sarah, Bruce H. Greenfield, Gail M. Jensen, Laura Lee Swisher, Nancy R. Kirsch, Carol Davis, and Ruth Purtilo. "Can Reading Tolstoy Make Us Better Physical Therapists? The Role of the Health Humanities in Physical Therapy." *Physical Therapy* 100, no. 6 (2020): 885–889.

Gabard, Donald L., and Mike W. Martin. *Physical Therapy Ethics*. 2nd ed. F.A. Davis Company, 2011.

Kirsch, Nancy. *Ethics in Physical Therapy: A Case-Based Approach*. McGraw-Hill Education, 2018.

Purtilo, Ruth. "A Time to Harvest, A Time to Sow: Ethics for a Shifting Landscape." *Physical Therapy* 80, no. 11 (2000): 1112–1119.

Purtilo, Ruth. "The American Physical Therapy Association's Code of Ethics." *Physical Therapy* 57, no. 9 (1977): 1001–1006.

Swisher, Laura Lee, Peggy Hiller, and the APTA Take Force to Revise the Core Ethics Documents. "The Revised APTA Code of Ethics for the Physical Therapist and Standards of Ethical Conduct for the Physical Therapy Assistant: Theory, Purpose, Process, and Significance." *Physical Therapy* 90, no. 5 (2010): 803–824.

Swisher, Laura Lee, and Catherine Page. *Professionalism in Physical Therapy: History, Practice, and Development*. Elsevier Saunders, 2005.

Swisher, Laura Lee, and Charlotte Brasic Royeen. *Rehabilitation Ethics for Interprofessional Practice*. Jones & Bartlett Learning, 2020.

Additional Readings for Unit III

Epstein, Elizabeth G., and Sarah Delgado. "Understanding and Addressing Moral Distress." *The Online Journal of Issues in Nursing* 15, no. 3 (2010). https://doi.org/10.3912/OJIN.Vol15No03Man01

Fourie, Carina. "Moral Distress and Moral Conflict in Clinical Ethics." *Bioethics* 29, no. 2 (2015): 91–97.

McAninch, Andrew. "Moral Distress, Moral Injury, and Moral Luck." *American Journal of Bioethics* 16, no. 12 (2016): 29–31.

Richardson, Robert W. "Ethical Issues in Physical Therapy." *Current Reviews in Musculoskeletal Medicine* 8 (2015): 118–121.

Thomas, Tessy Ann, and Courtenay Rose Bruce. "Moral Distress: Professional Integrity as the Basis for Taxonomies." *The American Journal of Bioethics* 16, no. 12 (2016): 11–13.

Thomas, Tessy Ann, and Laurence B. McCullough. "A Philosophical Taxonomy of Ethically Significant Moral Distress." *Journal of Medicine and Philosophy* 40 (2015): 102–120.

Ulrich, Connie M., Ann B. Hamric, and Christine Grady. "Moral Distress: A Growing Problem in the Health Professions?" *Hastings Center Report* 40, no. 1 (2010): 20–22.

Wilkinson, Judith M. "Moral Distress in Nursing Practice: Experience and Affects." *Nursing Forum* 23, no. 1 (1987/88): 16–29.

Additional Readings for Unit IV

Beresford, Eric B. "Uncertainty and the Shaping of Medical Decisions." *Hastings Center Report* 21, no. 4 (1991): 6–11.

Ditwiler, Rebecca E., Laura L. Swisher, and Dustin D. Hardwick. "Professional and Ethical Issues in United States Acute Care Physical Therapists Treating Patients with COVID-19: Stress, Walls, and Uncertainty." *Physical Therapy* 101, no. 8 (2020). https://doi.org/10.1093/ptj/pzab122

Djulbegovic, Benjamin, Iztok Hozo, and Sander Greenland. "Uncertainty in Clinical Medicine." In Handbook of the Philosophy of Science. Vol. 16, Philosophy of Medicine, edited by Fred Gifford, 299–356. Elsevier, 2011.

Eddy, David M. "Variations in Physical Practice: The Role of Uncertainty." *Health Affairs* 3 (1984): 74–89.

Fox, Renée C. "The Evolution of Medical Uncertainty." *Milbank Memorial Fund Quarterly/Health and Society* 58, no. 1 (1980): 1–49.

Hahn, Paul K. J., William M. P. Klein, and Neeraj K. Arora. "Varieties of Uncertainty in Health Care: A Conceptual Taxonomy." Medical Decision Making 31, no. 6 (2011): 828–838.

Healy, Tara C. "Ethical Decision Making: Pressure and Uncertainty as Complicating Factors." *Health & Social Work* 28, no. 4 (2003): 293–301.

Kahneman, Daniel. *Thinking Fast and Slow.* New York: Farra, Straus and Giroux, 2011.

Koffman, Jonathan, Jamie Gross, and Simon Noah Etkind. "Uncertainty and COVID-19: How are we to respond?" *Journal of the Royal Society of Medicine* 113, no. 6 (2020): 211–216.

Pomare, Chiara, Kate Churruca, Louise A. Ellis, Janet C. Long, and Jeffrey Braithwaite. "A revised model of uncertainty in complex healthcare settings: A scoping review." *Journal of Evaluative Clinical Practice 25* (2019): 176–182.

Roberts, Robert C., and Jay W. Wood. "Humility and Epistemic Goods." In *Intellectual Virtue: Perspectives in Ethics and Epistemology,* edited by Michael DePaul and Linda Zagzebski, 257–280. Oxford University Press, 2003.

Additional Readings for Unit V

Best, Jennifer. "Instilling Hope and Respecting Patient Autonomy: Reconciling Apparently Conflicting Duties." *Bioethics* 19, no. 3 (2005): 215–231.

Graves, Robert. *The Greek Myths: Complete and Unabridged.* Moyer Bell Limited, 1955.

Green, Rochelle M. *Theories of Hope.* Lexington Books, 2019.

Groopman, Jerome. *The Anatomy of Hope.* Random House, 2004.

Lear, Jonathan. *Radical Hope: Ethics in the Face of Cultural Devastation.* Harvard University Press, 2006.

Martin, Adrienne M. "Hope and Exploitation." *Hastings Center Report 38,* no. 5 (2008): 49–55.

McGeer, Victoria. "The Art of Good Hope." Annals of the American Academy of Political and Social Sciences 592 (2004): 100–127.

Meirav, Ariel. "The Nature of Hope." *Ratio* 22, no. 2 (2009): 216–233.

Simpson, Christy. "When Hope Makes Us Vulnerable: A Discussion of Patient-Healthcare Provider Interactions in the Context of Hope." *Bioethics* 18, no. 5 (2004): 428–447.

Snow, Nancy E. "Faces of Hope." In *Theories of Hope.* Edited by Rochelle M. Green. Lanham, MD: Lexington Books, 2019.

Stempsey, William E. "Hope for Health and Health Care." *Medicine, Health Care and Philosophy 18* (2015): 41–49.

Wallace, Robert W. "Why Did Hope Remain in Pandora's Jar?" *Teoria* 33, no. 2 (2013): 55–63.

Woolfrey, Joan. "The Infectiousness of Hope." *Philosophy in the Contemporary World 22,* no. 2 (2015): 94–103.

Additional Readings for Unit VI

Allingham, Michael. *Distributive Justice.* Routledge, 2014.

Anderson, Elizabeth. "What is the Point of Equality?" *Ethics* 109, no. 2 (1999): 287–337.

Arneson, Richard. "Equality and Equal Opportunity for Welfare." *Philosophical Studies* (1989): 77–93.

Beauchamp, Tom L., and James F. Childress. *Principles of Biomedical Ethics.* 6th ed. Oxford University Press, 2009.

Borges, Jorge Luis. "Lottery in Babylon." Translated by John M. Fein. *Prairie Schooner* 33, no. 3 (1959): 203–207.

Dworkin, Richard. *Sovereign Virtue*. Harvard University Press, 2000.

Edwards, Ian, Clare M. Delany, Anne F. Townsend, and Laura Lee Swisher. "Moral Agency as Enacted Justice: A Clinical and Ethical Decision-Making Framework for Responding to Health Inequities and Social Injustice" *APTA Physical Therapy Journal* 91, no. 11 (2011): 1653–1663.

Edwards, Ian, Clare M. Delany, Anne F. Townsend, and Laura Lee Swisher. "New Perspectives on the Theory of Justice: Implications for Physical Therapy Ethics and Clinical Practice." *APTA Physical Therapy Journal* 91, no. 11 (2011): 1642–1652.

Nozick, Robert. *Anarchy, State and Utopia*. Blackwell Publishing, 1974.

Nussbaum, Martha. *Frontiers of Justice: Disability, Nationality, Species Membership*. Harvard University Press, 2006.

Okin, Susan M. *Justice, Gender, and the Family*. Basic Books, 1989.

Rawls, John. *Justice as Fairness: A Restatement*. Harvard University Press, 2001.

Rhodes, Rosamond. "Justice and Guidance for the COVID-19 Pandemic." *The American Journal of Bioethics* 20, no. 7 (2020): 163–166.

Sen, Amartya. "Equality of What?" In *Tanner Lectures on Human Values*. Edited by S. McMurrin. Cambridge University Press, 1980.

Additional Readings for Unit VII

Boorse, Christopher. "On the Distinction Between Disease and Illness." *Philosophy and Public Affairs* 5 (1975): 49–68.

Canguilhem, Georges. *The Normal and the Pathological*. Zone Books, 1991.

Carel, Havi. *Phenomenology of Illness*. Oxford University Press, 2016.

Carel, Havi, and Rachel Cooper. *Health, Illness, and Disease: Philosophical Essays*. Taylor & Francis Group, 2014.

Cassell, Eric J. *The Nature of Suffering and the Goals of Medicine*. Oxford University Press, 1991.

Engelhardt, H. Tristram. "The Concepts of Health and Disease." In *Evaluation and Explanation in the Biomedical Sciences*. Edited by H. T. Engelhardt Jr. and S. F. Spicker, 125–141. Dordrecht, Netherlands: Reidel, 1975.

Foucault, Michel. *The Birth of the Clinic: An Archaeology of Medical Perception*. Vintage Books, 1973.

Greenfield, Bruce H., and Gail F. Jenson. "Understanding the Lived Experiences of Patients: Application of a Phenomenological Approach to Ethics." *Physical Therapy 90*, no. 8 (2010): 1185–1197.

Greenfield, Bruce H., Erin Keough, Sydney Lynn, Derek Little, and Christine Portela. "The Meaning of Caring from the Perspective of Patients Undergoing Physical Therapy." *Journal of Allied Health* 39, no. 2 (2010): 43–47.

Kovacs, Jozsef. "Concepts of Health and Disease." *The Journal of Medicine and Philosophy* 14 (1989): 261–267.

Moravcsik, Julius. "Ancient and Modern Conceptions of Health and Medicine." *The Journal of Medicine and Philosophy* 1 (1976): 337–348.

Toombs, S. Kay. *The Meaning of Illness: A Phenomenological Account of the Different Perspectives of Physician and Patient.* Heidelberg, Springer, 1992.

ABOUT THE EDITOR

Katherine K. Johnson, PhD, is an associate professor of philosophy and director of the Ethics and Social Justice Center at Bellarmine University in Louisville, KY. Katherine earned a BA in philosophy from Providence College and an MA and PhD in philosophy from Loyola University Chicago.